Praise for System Change

"The people's climate movement is a system change movement or it is nothing at all. This short book explains why. Everyone in the movement, and everyone considering joining the movement, needs a copy."
John Bellamy Foster, author of *Marx's Ecology*

"This critical collection of writing by ecosocialist thinkers helps explain why ecological crises — from climate change and massive biodiversity loss to soil degradation and toxic pollution — continue to accelerate despite the fact that policy-makers and businessmen have known for decades the deadly ecological and social consequences of continuing so much business and politics "as usual". Just as importantly, the writers offer real hope and a way forward. They allow us to imagine a world in which life can not only survive, which is now in question for too many species and communities around the world, but thrive. And they tell us how to get there."
Hannah Holleman, author of *Dust Bowls of Empire: Imperialism, Environmental Politics, and the Injustice of "Green" Capitalism*

"A highly readable collection of essays clarifying the systemic causes of environmental degradation and why a new economic/social system is essential to the future of humanity and many other species. An important addition to the ecosocialist literature."
Fred Magdoff, co-author of *What Every Environmentalist Needs to Know About Capitalism* and *Creating an Ecological Society*

"This collection blends scientific expertise, political organising experience, and long-term vision in a way that will be of great value for crafting an effective response to the ecological crisis. The authors show the negative implications of policy approaches inspired by capitalist precepts such as the attempt to put prices on natural goods. They discuss in detail the implications of proposals that stress organic agriculture and/or a vegan diet. They provide a sound overview of the theoretical positions that underlie current debates in the movement. Readers will be well equipped to educate people about both the urgency and the practical dimensions of our collective struggle for survival."
Victor Wallis, author of *Red-Green Revolution: The Politics and Technology of Ecosocialism*

"Informed by the latest work of earth-system science and Marxist ecology, this collection of articles by leading ecosocialist scholars and activists emphasises the multifaceted character of the biospheric crisis perpetrated by capitalism — from climate change, to declining biodiversity, to agriculture and food crises, to the plastics problem. At the same time, it effectively counters mainstream "natural capital" and other "green capitalism" approaches that try to further incorporate nature into the same system of market prices and capital accumulation that is destroying the planet as a living system. The authors clearly demonstrate the need for an economic system directly serving human needs, based on cooperative and democratic systems of worker-community control, in order to heal the rift with nature created by capitalist management and markets."
Paul Burkett, author of *Marx and Nature* and *Marxism and Ecological Economics*

"The book includes cutting edge analysis of climate change, plastic, fossil fuels, agriculture, biodiversity, inequality and the current crisis of the earth's natural systems from some of the world's best activists and writers. But most importantly, the book puts forward a set of tools to analyse how capitalism has dragged us into this mess, and how to develop the movements and the power we need to prevent catastrophe and reorganise human society on a sustainable basis. It is essential reading for any social justice or environmental activist in the 21st century."
Penny McCall Howard, author of *Environment, Labour and Capitalism at Sea*

"As its title indicates the contributors to this edited collection are united in their recognition of the climate crisis as a crisis with intrinsic connections to capitalism as a social and economic system. They are also united in drawing strongly on recent US interpretations of Marx's later work, giving central place to the analysis of capitalism's inherently disruptive impact on nature, generating multiple 'metabolic rifts'. Many of the international constellation of authors brought together here are already well-known for their substantive development of these ideas in relation not just to climate change, but also the alarming rate of extinction of species, the state of capitalist agriculture and the food system, soil degradation, oceanic pollution, the fossil fuel economy, and the debate concerning the proposed new geological epoch — the Anthropocene. Although the perspective is held in common, there is enough original argument and independent judgement to make this an important and enlightening read. The conclusion is clear, however, that, as someone once said, 'the point is to change it'."
Ted Benton, red-green activist and natural history writer

System Change not Climate Change
A Revolutionary Response to Environmental Crisis

Edited by *Martin Empson*
With contributions from *Ian Angus, Carolyn Egan, Sarah Ensor,
Suzanne Jeffery, Amy Leather, Ian Rappel, Michelle Robidoux,
Camilla Royle* and *Kohei Saito*

System Change not Climate Change

A Revolutionary Response to Environmental Crisis

Edited by Martin Empson

With contributions from Ian Angus, Carolyn Egan, Sarah Ensor,
Suzanne Jeffery, Amy Leather, Ian Rappel, Michelle Robidoux,
Camilla Royle and Kohei Saito

Published 2019

© Bookmarks Publications c/o 1 Bloomsbury Street, London, WC1B 3QE

Chapter 3: The Discovery and Rediscovery of Metabolic Rift © Ian Angus

Designed and typeset by Simon Assaf

Cover design by Bookmarks Publications

Printed by Halstan

ISBN (pbk) 9781912926183

ISBN (Kindle) 9781912926190

ISBN (ePub) 9781912926206

ISBN (PDF) 9781912926213

Authors

Ian Angus is editor of the online ecosocialist journal *Climate and Capitalism*. He is the author of *Facing the Anthropocene* (Monthly Review, 2016) and *A Redder Shade of Green* (Monthly Review, 2017). His new book, *Metabolic Rifts*, will be published by Monthly Review in 2020.

Carolyn Egan is president of United Steelworkers Local 8300 and a member of the International Socialists Canada. She is co-chair of the Toronto Good Jobs For All Coalition, which brings together trade unionists, members of communities of colour and environmentalists to link the economic crisis, the climate crisis and the question of racism and equity in the fight for a just transition to climate jobs.

Martin Empson is a member of the Socialist Workers Party and an environmental activist with the Campaign Against Climate Change. He is the author of *Land and Labour: Marxism, Ecology and Human History* (Bookmarks, 2014) and *'Kill All the Gentlemen': Class Struggle and Change in the English Countryside* (Bookmarks, 2018).

Sarah Ensor researches the history of the working class in Iceland and worked for six years in Iceland's fishing industry. Her blog is at *www.herringandclassstruggle.blogspot.co.uk*

Suzanne Jeffery is a longstanding member of the Socialist Workers Party and involved in the Campaign Against Climate Change in the UK. She helped organise the Time to Act climate protests in 2015 and has been involved with the One Million Climate Jobs campaign for many years.

Amy Leather is the joint National Secretary of the Socialist Workers Party.

Ian Rappel is a conservation ecologist and member of the Socialist Workers Party. He is also a member of the Beyond Extinction Economics (BEE) network.

Michelle Robidoux is a socialist and a climate justice activist.

Camilla Royle is a member of the Socialist Workers Party and deputy editor of *International Socialism*. She has a PhD in geography from King's College London.

Kohei Saito teaches at Osaka City University and is the author of *Karl Marx's Ecosocialism: Capital, Nature, and the Unfinished Critique of Political Economy* (Monthly Review, 2017), which won the 2018 Isaac and Tamara Deutscher Memorial Prize.

Acknowledgements

Thanks to Colm Bryce at Bookmarks Publications, Simon Assaf, Carol Williams, Sally Campbell and Yuri Prasad for their work on this book. Several of the chapters are updated and expanded versions of articles that were first published elsewhere. Thanks to Climate and Capitalism (*https://climateandcapitalism.com*), Socialist Review (*www.socialistreview.org.uk*) and International Socialism (*www.isj.org.uk*) for permission to republish them.

Contents

Introduction
Why We Need System Change
Martin Empson

As we approach the third decade of the 21st century, humanity faces an existential threat. Multiple environmental crises — most notably climate change and the destruction of biodiversity — threaten the very basis of our society. The authors in this book argue that the cause of these catastrophic threats is the nature of capitalist society. It is a system which puts the profits of businesses and multinational corporations before the long term interests of people and the planet that they live on.

This book was put together in the early months of 2019. The previous year saw heat waves across the globe. In many parts of the world there were unprecedented temperatures. The immediate effects of these were localised in the sense that different countries experienced and reacted differently; but from the Americas to Asia, from the Arctic Circle to Africa millions of people experienced a hotter world. In 2018 the impact of a warming world could be felt in places as varied as North America, where temperatures broke record after record, and in Sweden, where numerous wild fires took hold even within in the Arctic Circle. In France some cities imposed travel bans to reduce air pollution that was worsened by the hot, still air. In Spain nine people died from the heat and between April and July Germany had average temperatures 3.6 degrees Celsius higher than 1961 to 1990.[1]

But these temperatures paled when compared to those experienced in parts of the Global South. In July 2018 Yerevan, Armenia, experienced a record high for the month of 42°C. In April, in Nawabshah, Pakistan one million people experienced a temperature of 50.2°C, and on 26 June in Quriyat, Oman, temperatures in one 24-hour period never dropped below 42.6°C — the highest minimum temperature ever recorded. The British Trades Union Congress argues that a temperature range of 22°C to 24°C is the "comfort zone" for working, and above this productivity falls. If blood temperature reaches 39 degrees "there is a risk of heat stroke or collapse". The TUC calls for a legal maximum temperature at work of 30°C (27°C for "strenuous work").[2]

These headline temperatures are part of a pattern of extremes in a warming world — more and more locations are experiencing hotter and hotter weather. But the crisis is not simply about temperature. As global warming increases temperatures the weather becomes more extreme, more unpredictable and individual events — whether hurricanes, heat waves, wildfires or droughts — become more intense. Seemingly paradoxically we also see periods of intense cold, such as the polar vortexes that hit the United States, as changing weather patterns drive intensely cold Arctic air southwards. These impacts will also drive further environmental and social crises — rising sea levels will flood coastal lands, ruining freshwater supplies, rendering agricultural land unusable, making some cities uninhabitable and requiring billions to be spent on flood defences. Even in the short term, the human consequences will be unimaginable.

In October 2018 the United Nations Intergovernmental Panel on Climate Change released a report that argued the world had only 12 years to keep the rise in global temperature to a maximum

1. BBC News, "Europe heatwave: High Temperatures but respite expected", 6 August 2018, *https://www.bbc.co.uk/news/world-europe-45089709*

2. TUC, *Heat – The Case for a Maximum Temperature at Work*, 2009.

of 1.5 degrees to avoid environmental disaster. Doing this would require, what the IPCC report has called "transformative systemic change". But despite decades of warnings there has been next to no serious action to avoid climate disaster. One author explained the cause of global warming and what needs to be done:

> This change is thought to have come about mainly as the result of burning fossil fuels... The output of these (and other) carbon dioxide sources is clearly outstripping the absorbing capacity of carbon dioxide "sinks"... If the surplus continues to increase at its present rate, CO_2 in the atmosphere promises to reach levels of over 650ppm in the next fifty years...scientists now generally agree that the present build-up of CO_2 in the atmosphere could, if it were to continue without restriction, spell catastrophe for our planet within less than a century. Exactly what to do about it must remain in question until we have more exact knowledge... But time is not on our side... How can a dangerous bottleneck of atmospheric carbon dioxide be avoided? The obvious answer is, by curbing the use of fossil fuels, but it is plainly an answer that today runs straight against the grain of real politics and economic habit.[3]

This passage was written by the conservationist Robert Lamb in 1979. Forty years ago he was entitled not be 100 percent sure about the exact causes of climate change and the required solutions. But in the ensuing decades the contributions of thousands of scientists mean we can confidently agree with his conclusion — the need to end the use of fossil fuels. Those politicians who tell us today that there is not a scientific consensus, or that we have only understood the problem recently are lying — the problem, and its causes have been understood for decades, and every year of inaction has worsened the crisis and

3. Robert Lamb, *A World Without Trees* (Wildwood House, 1979), pp36-40.

condemned millions of people to suffering.

The victims of the environmental crisis are the poorest and most vulnerable in society. This unequal impact of climate change is, in part, the result of the development of capitalism itself. Countries like Britain and the United States grew rich by robbing the rest of the globe of its natural resources and people. As Karl Marx pointed out in *Capital*:

> The discovery of gold and silver in America, the extirpation, enslavement and entombment in mines of the aboriginal population, the beginning of the conquest and looting of the East Indies, the turning of Africa into a warren for the commercial hunting of black-skins, signalised the rosy dawn of the era of capitalist production. These idyllic proceedings are the chief momenta of primitive accumulation.[4]

As capitalism expanded across the globe it concentrated wealth in a few countries, and a system of fossil fuel capitalism developed which rapidly expanded around the world.

But climate change also impacts unequally because of the structure of capitalist society. Even in rich countries the poorest are hit first and worst by climate change. Environmental crisis exacerbates all the fault-lines and fractures within capitalism. Wherever you are in the world, if you are poor, black or female you are more likely to be the victim of climate change. This is even acknowledged by the United Nations:

> Disasters tend to hit the poorest and most marginalized demographics the hardest. Women and girls are particularly exposed to climate-related disaster risk — they are likely to suffer higher rates of mortality, morbidity and economic damage to their livelihoods.[5]

4. Karl Marx, *Capital vol. 1* (Penguin, 1990), p915.

5. Senay Habtezion, *Gender and Disaster Risk Reduction* (United Nations Development Programme, 2013).

In a disaster, the UN concluded, women and children are 14 times more likely to be victims. This is true even in the developed world — in the 2003 European heatwave, more women died than men. Similarly, black and Asian communities are more likely to be sited in areas of vulnerability to environmental disaster. When Hurricane Katrina hit New Orleans in 2005, those who were left behind and trapped in the Superdome were overwhelmingly black. They were demonised as looters, and wrongly accused of rape and violence, as they struggled to survive in the aftermath.

Similarly, when Hurricane Sandy hit New York in 2012, those who suffered most from the blackouts and loss of services were predominantly from the poorest neighbourhoods, which meant that black people were particularly badly hit.

Environmental disaster also leads to people fleeing their homes. The term "climate refugee" is often applied to those fleeing from the effects of global warming, environmental disaster or consequent social collapse. It's a term that has as yet no legal definition, yet millions of people already have the label. As Ashley Dawson has recently argued in his book *Extreme Cities*:

> The Internal Displacement Monitoring Centre calculates that 192.3 million people from 113 countries were displaced because of disasters in 2015, "more than twice the number who fled conflict and violence".[6]

The floods in Pakistan in 2010, to take one example, led to one million people becoming refugees, people who were then prone to malaria and other diseases as they waited for assistance. In the United States around one million people fled Hurricane Katrina and Hurricane Sandy displaced 776,000 people.[7] Despite promises made in the midst of crisis, these people were quickly forgotten. Eleven years after Katrina, in

6. Ashley Dawson, *Extreme Cities* (Verso, 2019), p191.

7. Dawson, *Extreme Cities*, p190.

the world's richest economy, one in three black residents had yet to return home and some areas still have less than half of their pre-disaster population. As one report says New Orleans did not have "an equal opportunity recovery".[8] In the aftermath of Sandy, veteran Civil Rights campaigner Al Sharpton argued powerfully against media use of the phrase refugee to describe the victims: "They are not refugees wandering somewhere looking for charity. They are victims of neglect and a situation they should never have been put in in the first place".[9]

This demonisation of the victims of disaster is a small indication of what we will see in the future. We already know from the 2015 refugee crisis that those fleeing war and disaster are prevented from seeking refuge. They are stopped at the borders by barbed wire and armed men, and governments and the media demonise and lie about the refugees to justify the refusal of assistance. As a result, the Mediterranean Sea has become a graveyard for thousands of men, women and children whose only crime was to hope for a better life.

The tragic irony is that the refugees come from countries that have done little or nothing to contribute to global warming. Because carbon dioxide can stay in the atmosphere for hundreds of years, it is the developed world that has contributed most to the current crisis. Britain contributed over 50 percent of carbon dioxide until the year 1883. As a result, Britain has been responsible for just over 5 percent of all historic emissions of CO_2. The United States has been responsible for 26 percent of historic emissions, and the 28 countries of the EU are responsible for just under 22 percent. The rapid transformation of the Chinese economy means that it is one of today's biggest emitters, but historically is only responsible for just under 13 percent of emissions.[10]

This means that the developed world has a historic debt to

8. https://talkpoverty.org/2016/08/29/white-new-orleans-recovered-hurricane-katrina-black-new-orleans-not/

9. Quoted in Dawson, *Extreme Cities*, p192.

10. Historic emissions data from Hannah Ritchie and Max Roser, "CO_2 and other Greenhouse Gas Emissions", Our World in Data, accessed March 2018 at https://ourworldindata.org/

the people of the whole globe. Countries like the US and those of Europe have created environmental disaster. But this is not to blame everyone. Since 1988 just 100 fossil fuel producers have been responsible for 71 percent of global emissions, and 52 percent of historic emissions.[11]

This helps us understand how to stop environmental disaster. Those who argue that we should change our individual lifestyles — giving up cars or flying, changing to a vegan or vegetarian diet — are missing the point. We need to challenge the very existence of those fossil fuel corporations and the system that needs them.

But capitalism is a fossil fuel system and the state will organise to protect the interests of capital. This contradiction means that at the same time as governments around the world promise action on the environment, they also hand out subsidies and support to the fossil fuel industry. Those who protest against pipelines or against fracking meet the full force of the state — through the police and the legal system.

The end of 2018 saw a global resurgence of the environmental movement. Protests by groups like Extinction Rebellion in the UK, or the wave of international student strikes, show that millions of people understand that to get change we need mass action. The popularity of the slogan "System Change Not Climate Change" also suggests that protesters understand we need fundamental change.

Climate change is closely linked to other environmental and social issues — it has a knock on effect in terms of species extinction and food production for instance. But all the environmental threats we face — whether it is plastic pollution in the oceans, air pollution in our cities, or dead zones in the sea due to agricultural chemicals — are caused and made worse by a system that puts profits before anything else. The chapters in this book explore the environmental crises we face, show how they are linked to the capitalist system and offer a strategy for radical change.

11. The Carbon Majors Database, CDP Report 2017, *www.cdp.net/en/articles/media/new-report-shows-just-100-companies-are-source-of-over-70-of-emissions*

Capitalism is a system that is inherently anti-ecological. It destroys the natural world that we all rely on and are part of. Because of this capitalism cannot solve the environmental crises that it has caused. In fact, capitalism's solutions make the situation worse, and only serve to further increase the profits of the multinationals. What is needed is revolutionary change.

Under capitalism it is the labour of ordinary working people that makes the system work. Karl Marx showed how the bosses make profits out of the exploitative relationship between the boss and the workers. The bosses' system relies completely on the labour of billions of ordinary men and women, and so it is these people who have the power to change society. When they stop work the system grinds to a halt. Without workers, trains don't run, cars aren't built, telephones aren't answered and food doesn't get grown or distributed.

Karl Marx did not know about global climate change. But he did understand that there was a link between capitalism and environmental destruction. He saw that without a revolution replacing capitalism with a system where production was based on a democratically planned economy, humanity was doomed to ongoing environmental crisis. That society — a socialist one where ordinary people organise collectively to rationally use the world's resources in the best interest of people and planet — is the only way we can ensure a sustainable future. This book is a contribution to the struggle for that future.

***

Chapter 1

Hopelessly Devoted to Fossil Fuels

Amy Leather

The last decade has seen a massive expansion of so called "dirty energies" such as fracking, deep water drilling, and tar sand extraction. The pledges to reduce carbon emissions in the Paris Agreement, signed by 196 countries in December 2015, are only voluntary. Even if signatories kept to them, we would still be on track for global warming far higher than is sustainable.[1]

The scale of the crisis is widely recognised. In August 2016 scientists from the Anthropocene Working Group argued that we have entered a new geological era — the Anthropocene — in which the dominant influence on the environment is human activity. Unless urgent action is taken we face catastrophic climate change. The report of 2018 from the UN Intergovernmental Panel on Climate Change (IPCC) warned that the earth's temperature rise must be kept to 1.5 degrees Celsius above pre-industrial levels. Previously it had been generally accepted that we needed to limit carbon emissions to keep the temperature

1. This is an updated version of an article that first appeared in *Socialist Review*, January 2017.

rise to two degrees. Temperatures have already increased by one degree on pre-industrial levels. The solution to global warming is quite simple — we need to stop burning fossil fuels, such as coal, oil and gas which release carbon dioxide into the atmosphere, and instead make a rapid switch to renewables.

The IPCC were clear that to eradicate carbon pollution and limit the temperature rise to 1.5 degrees "presented governments with pretty hard choices" and would require an "unprecedented shift in energy systems and transport". However they were clear it could be done: "We show it can be done within laws of physics and chemistry...the final tick box is political will."

So why won't our rulers act? We need to look beyond the individual politicians. There are, of course, the climate change deniers, who must be challenged and stopped, but much of the ruling class does accept that climate change is a reality. The problem is they are guardians of a system with fossil fuels at its heart. The history of industrial capitalism is entwined with the growth and development of the fossil fuel industry. Tackling the climate crisis would mean tackling the vested interests of the fossil fuel corporations — some of the most profitable companies in the world. Fossil fuels such as coal, oil and gas are completely locked into capitalism. To understand why capitalism and fossil fuels are so intertwined we need to go back to the time of the industrial revolution in Britain.

Andreas Malm, in his book *Fossil Capital*, outlines how in the early 1800s, an energy transition took place in Britain. The first machines of the industrial revolution, the spinning and weaving machines of the cotton industry, were driven by water. In 1800 there were at least 1,000 water mills concentrated in Lancashire and Scotland. Even as late as the 1820s most mills in Manchester were still water-powered. However, just ten years later steam generated by burning coal had overtaken water and become the predominant form of power.

This transition to steam was not an inevitable consequence of James Watt's invention of the rotative steam engine in 1784.

A protracted battle took place in industry. Water's main advantage was that it was free, as well as being abundant in the rain soaked areas of Scotland and the north west of England, where the cotton industry was based. But steam allowed capitalists to exploit labour more efficiently. Coal was mobile. The capitalist could move it to where the labour sources were, rather than having to move people to where the energy source was.

Water-powered mills or factories had to be built next to the water source. A disciplined workforce was hard to find in such rural areas and so the mill owners would have to invest in building a "colony" — a settlement near the water source to house and service workers. This was both an extra outlay and an invitation to industrial strife. In contrast coal was a "ticket to the town" giving capitalists better access to disciplined workers in the newly expanded urban areas. The cost of coal began to be offset by these benefits.

A number of factors came together in the 1820s and 1830s. The Factory Acts, which limited working hours, had a greater impact on the factories powered by water. Previously, if these mills lost production time due to a lack of water supply, they would make it up by imposing longer hours to offset the lost production. Once this avenue was closed the advantage began to fall to steam.

So the fossil economy has one incontestable birthplace: Britain. However, this wasn't a collective decision by the whole British population. In fact, the introduction of steam was often fiercely resisted by workers, such as in the Plug Plot Riots of 1842, which were linked to the Chartist movement. Workers pulled the plugs out of the steam engines, stopping production by allowing the water to escape.

The introduction of steam unleashed a process, a path of development, with fossil fuels at its heart. The nature of capitalist competition meant that once one capitalist introduced a new method others were forced to follow in order to keep up. The shift to coal didn't stay confined to Britain. Economic and military competition meant that the fossil economy was soon projected across the globe. By the end of the 19th century industry and railroads in the US were burning more coal than those in Britain, while Germany and a number of other European countries were also about to catch up.

The introduction of oil further drove this process. Petroleum had previously been used mainly for lighting as kerosene and as lubrication. The inventions of the internal combustion engine in the 1880s and of the aeroplane in 1903 created a new market for it. These new machines used gasoline — a part of petroleum that refiners had been previously discarding. In the early 20th century imperial armies became major customers for gasoline. Oil-powered tanks, aeroplanes, warships and submarines played decisive roles in the First World War.

One breakthrough for petroleum was Britain's decision in 1912 to convert its battleships from coal to oil. Class interests played a major role in the decision. The only source of the high grade anthracite coal that fuelled battleships was the Welsh mines. In 1910 Winston Churchill had used the army to break strikes in these pits. When he took responsibility for the army in 1911, he immediately initiated a programme to convert the battleships to oil. He said that in doing this the government "was freeing itself from the political claims of the miners".

Shortly after the First World War mass production of cars began. By 1929 the car industry was the largest in the US. Meanwhile the chemical industry was developing new products made either from the by-products of oil refining or requiring the high levels of energy that only oil could provide. The 1930s saw the invention of synthetic fibres such as nylon and the first mass-produced plastics and industrial chemicals.

From the 1880s onwards the concentration and centralisation of capital saw giant companies dominating the global economy — nowhere more so than in the fossil industries. In 1930 over half of the 200 largest industrial companies in the US were in the chemicals, petroleum, metals, rubber or transportation industries. Such concentrated power meant that decisions made in a handful of enterprises could rapidly change whole industries and affect the entire world.

In his book *Facing the Anthropocene*, Ian Angus points to "the Great Acceleration" in global warming that took place after 1945. Total world energy consumption more than tripled in the post-war period. The conditions for this were shaped by developments made during the Second World War. The US government pumped massive amounts of money into oil-related industries to help the war effort. Six out of every seven barrels of oil used by the Allied Forces came from US wells and were refined by US oil companies. The government built new pipelines and refineries equipped with new technology. The US car industry stopped commercial production and instead made 2 million jeeps and trucks plus aeroplane engines, tanks, armoured cars, machine guns and bombs — funded by $29 billion in government subsidies. These industries ended the war with updated and expanded facilities, which laid the basis for a massive expansion of production.

The US government also ploughed money into the petrochemical plants to produce nitrogen for explosives, synthetic rubber for tyres and nylon for parachutes. After the war the government sold these new updated factories and plants at knock down prices to private oil and chemical companies, not only encouraging further use of fossil fuels but also paving the way for a new age of plastic. This state-led renewal of manufacturing had enormous implications for both the global role of the US and the use of fossil fuels.

The Marshall Plan of 1948 strengthened the global role of US corporations. The US state gave vast amounts of money to European countries so they could buy oil from US oil companies. Between 1948 and 1951 more than half of the oil sold to Western European buyers by US oil companies was paid for with Marshall Plan funds. The US government also subsidised the expansion of its oil companies into new facilities in Saudi Arabia in order to meet European demand. Before the war 20 percent of Europe's oil imports came from the Middle East, rising to 85 percent in

1950. This setup accelerated Europe's long-term transition from coal to oil dependence. World oil production grew by more than 700 percent in the period 1946-73.

The Second World War fundamentally shaped the terrain, enabling the growth of massive corporations in the fossil fuel economy. Other trends drove this further, such as the industrialisation of agriculture with its use of synthetic fertilisers and pesticides derived from oil. Today's food system is reliant on fossil fuel inputs at every stage of production, distribution, packaging and consumption. Continued high military expenditure after the war also had an impact. Today the US military is the world's largest user of petroleum, the largest polluter — producing more hazardous waste than the five largest US chemical companies combined — and the largest producer of greenhouse gases.

The whole infrastructure of capitalism has been built on fossil fuel. These enormous historic investments would have to be written off if we were to make a transition to renewables. Such a vast global write-off of capital would be unprecedented in scale. Globally the replacement cost of the existing fossil fuel and nuclear power infrastructure runs into trillions of dollars. It is unlikely that companies operating it would be happy to write off that amount and replace it with a renewable energy system carrying an even higher price tag.

Capitalists want to retrieve their costs. Even once the cost of, for example, a power plant has been recovered, it is still better to keep it in operation for as long as possible. Decommissioning the structure and constructing another would be to start all over again and lose any market advantage. Two thirds of US power plants built since the 1890s are still in use.

Capital has a vested interest in the endurance of the fossil fuel landscape. Although it is rational from the point of view of the planet to switch to renewables, it is completely irrational from the point of view of each individual capitalist. And, of course, the fossil fuel industries have plenty of money to ensure they do continue. Naomi Klein in her book, *This Changes Everything*, exposed the vast lobbying power of these companies. In 2013 in the US alone the oil and gas industries spent $400,000 every day lobbying Congress and government officials. The problem gets worse as time goes on. Investment in fossil industries doesn't stop while governments argue over what to do about emissions. When and if the decision is finally made to cut emissions seriously, far more capital will have to be liquidated than if the process had been started decades ago. In the first decade of the new millennium more coal fired power plants were constructed than in any previous decade. In the three years from 2010 to 2012 more than two and a half times more coal capacity was added than in the entire decade of the 1990s.

As Angus makes clear, "Fossil fuels are not an overlay that can be peeled away from capitalism — leaving the system intact, they are embedded in every aspect of the system." It is common within the climate movement to hear the argument that we are all to blame for climate change. However, it is clear that the decisions to adopt fossil fuels and continue and expand their use were not made by everyone. Rather the decision was made by those early capitalists at the start of industrialisation in Britain as a way to better exploit workers in order to maximise profit.

Of course, those capitalists in the 1830s could not have known they were setting the world on course for catastrophic global warming — although it is worth noting that air quality and related issues were subject to much complaint by the working class at the time. But the point is we now know the consequences of burning coal, oil and gas.

Yet the irrationality of capitalism dictates the opposite of the action that needs to be taken. This is not a technical problem. Studies show that a full transition to renewable, non-carbon fuels is physically possible. Of course, it would cost money but, as we've seen, states have made investments on this scale before, particularly during wartime. But the historic investment in the fossil fuel industries and the colossal vested interests with the power to lobby governments mean that we are up against massive economic and political obstacles.

If we accept that fossil fuels are completely embedded in capitalism then the conclusion must surely be that we have to get rid of that system. We need to make real the slogan "system change not climate change". We need to talk about real socialist transformation where production is for need not profit, and where the vast majority of people have democratic control over resources, production and the economy.

But this is not an argument for us to wait until the revolution to sort out climate change. The problem is immediate. There are battles constantly within capitalism. Sometimes there are struggles explicitly about climate change and the environment, for example over fracking in Britain. Campaigning against fracking in the UK has made a difference; it has helped stop the further expansion of the fossil fuel landscape. As more reports come out about the impact of climate change and need for action becomes clearer it is likely that there will be more such action.

It is also true that battles in capitalism can arise over other issues but become linked to that of climate. Crucially they can show the power to take on those vested interests of the oil and gas companies. Strikes by workers in oil refineries and fuel depots, or collective action by distribution workers in the oil and gas industries can hit the profits of even the biggest multinational.

In 2016 a sustained protest at Standing Rock in Dakota saw a victory, with the US engineer corps saying it will not allow a massive oil pipeline to be routed beneath the Missouri River. But other fights can also show the power to take on those vested interests of the oil and gas companies. Also in 2016, strikes in France over a new work law took place in oil refineries and involved blockades of fuel depots. The action led to a petrol shortage and hit power output. The strikes showed where power lies to take on the giant fossil fuel multinationals.

In every movement wider questions are raised about capitalism and where power lies in society to bring about change. As revolutionaries and environmentalists we should be part of every fight over the issue of the climate — as well as raising the question of climate change in every struggle. The impact of climate change intensifies all struggles bred by capitalism. We have to be part of those struggles, link them together and crucially connect them to the power to get rid of capitalism completely. We have to fight now to stop the further expansion of fossil fuels but we also need to fight to replace a society based on accumulation for profit with one based on production for need.

***

Chapter 2
Marxism and the Anthropocene
Camilla Royle

As you read this chapter every breath you take in contains about 410 parts per million (ppm) of carbon dioxide, around a third more than your great grandparents breathed 100 years ago.[1] As well as leading to potentially catastrophic global warming, carbon dioxide in the atmosphere has changed the way plants photosynthesise and has also made seas and lakes more acidic, more so than they have been for the last 800,000 years.[2] The effect human activity is having on the world is on such a huge scale that, for a growing number of thinkers, earth has entered a new geological epoch defined by human influence. Using the Greek word Anthropos (human) they propose to name this epoch the Anthropocene. The reality of the Anthropocene is becoming quite widely accepted. Two scientists, Simon Lewis and Mark Maslin state that "it

1. Go to *www.co2.earth*. This chapter benefitted from feedback from Alex Callinicos, Joseph Choonara, Martin Empson and Ian Rappel. It was originally published in *International Socialism* 151 in July 2016 and updated in early 2019, by which time the concentration of CO_2 had risen by 10ppm.

2. Simon Lewis, "A Force of Nature: Our Influential Anthropocene Period", Guardian, 23 July 2009, *www.theguardian.com/commentisfree/cif-green/2009/jul/23/climate-change-humanity-change*

is difficult to find a scientist who disagrees with the central Anthropocene claim: that humans have radically changed the Earth as an integrated system". [3]

This is not just about carbon dioxide emissions. Plastic, invented not much more than 100 years ago, now forms huge swirling islands in the oceans, and plastic and aluminium waste, which one study refers to as "technofossils", can be found in sediments. [4] The invention of synthetic fertilisers has meant that more nitrogen is now being added to the environment by humans than by all other processes; this has allowed levels of nitrogen and phosphorous in soils to double in the past century. [5] Radionucleotides produced by nuclear energy and nuclear weapons testing can also be detected in the soil. [6] And species extinction is at least 100 times higher than it would be without human intervention. These changes can be detected across vast areas of the earth, the seas, the atmosphere and in the bodies of living things. And all of them would not have taken place without humans. The Anthropocene means an uncertain future, where human activity is in danger of pushing planetary conditions away from a "safe operating space" for humanity towards a completely different type of world to which human societies may not even have time to adapt. [7]

The term "Anthropocene" has been popularised by two Earth System scientists, Paul Crutzen and Eugene Stoermer. They used the word in a short article in 2000 for the newsletter

---

3. Simon Lewis and Mark Maslin, *The Human Planet: How we Created the Anthropocene* (Pelican, 2018).

4. Jan Zalasiewicz, and many others, "When did the Anthropocene begin? A mid-twentieth century boundary level is stratigraphically optimal", *Quaternary International*, volume 383, 2015.

5. Adam Vaughan, "Human impact has pushed Earth into the Anthropocene, scientists say", Guardian, 7 January 2016, *www.theguardian.com/environment/2016/jan/07/human-impact-has-pushed-earth-into-the-anthropocene-scientists-say*

6. Richard Monastersky, "First atomic blast proposed as start of Anthropocene", *Nature News*, 16 January 2015, *www.nature.com/news/first-atomic-blast-proposed-as-start-of-anthropocene-1.16739*

7. Ian Angus, "Entering the Age of Humans", *Socialist Review*, May 2016, *http://socialistreview.org.uk/413/entering-age-humans*

of the International Geosphere-Biosphere Programme.[8] Geologists conventionally divide up historical time into eons, eras, periods, epochs and ages. Currently we are in the Phanerozoic eon, the Cenozoic era and the quaternary period. The quaternary is divided further into two epochs: Pleistocene and Holocene. The Pleistocene was marked by huge climatic fluctuations and repeated ice ages in the Northern hemisphere. The Holocene began the last time the glaciers retreated.[9] For Crutzen and Stoermer, humans have recently become a much more significant force than in the Holocene and are likely to "remain a major geological force for many millennia, maybe millions of years, to come".[10]

"What matters when dividing geological-scale time is global-scale changes to Earth's status, driven by causes as varied as meteor strikes, the movement of continents and sustained volcanic eruptions".[11] For some, humanity's effect on the planet is so profound that it can be likened to such events. For others, humanity is so deeply implicated in planetary processes that we are a constant presence; we are like the weather.[12] As Simon Lewis points out, the diagnosis of the Anthropocene represents a shift in the way humanity sees itself. Scientists in the past have shown humanity how insignificant we are; Copernicus discovered that we are not the centre of the universe and Charles Darwin showed that we are not at the top of an evolutionary hierarchy. But now "the future direction of the only place in the universe where we know life exists is in our hands. Suddenly,

8. Paul Crutzen and Eugene Stoermer, "The 'Anthropocene'", International Geosphere-Biosphere Programme (IGBP) Global Change Newsletter, number 41, May 2000. The IGBP was itself set up in 1987 as a result of an increasing realisation of the need to study the interactions between human societies and Earth's physical, chemical and biological processes, often described as a singular "Earth system" www.igbp.net/

9. Ian Angus, "The Anthropocene: When did it begin and why does it matter?" Monthly Review, volume 67, number 4, 2015.

10. Crutzen and Stoermer, "The 'Anthropocene'", as above, p18.

11. Simon Lewis and Mark Maslin, "Defining the Anthropocene", Nature, issue 519, 2015.

12. The term "human weather" is associated with Erle Ellis. See Erle Ellis, "Evolving toward a better Anthropocene", Future Earth blog (29 March 2016), www.futureearth.org/blog/2016-mar-29/evolving-toward-better-anthropocene.

after almost 500 years, humanity is centre stage again".[13]

Since 2000 the usage of the term Anthropocene has spread far beyond the small group of scientists who came up with the idea. Numerous blogs discussing the Anthropocene have been set up, articles written and events held to discuss the issue. The idea has also captured the imagination of artists like Jason deCaires Taylor, whose 2011 piece "Anthropocene" is an underwater sculpture of a Volkswagen Beetle with a girl curled up on the windscreen. The sculpture demonstrates the connection between human-made items and the lives of other species by acting as an artificial reef that is designed to attract lobsters to come and live inside it.[14]

For socialists, the Anthropocene can prompt us to rethink our ideas about the relationship between humans and (the rest of) nature, the role scientists might play in progressive politics and the centrality of environmental ideas to Marxist theory. However, the idea has not been universally accepted by Marxists. Some, such as John Bellamy Foster and Ian Angus, endorse the concept of the Anthropocene wholeheartedly.[15] As Foster points out, in the Soviet Union geologists Aleksei Pavlov and Vladimir Vernadsky both developed an understanding of the role of human agency in environmental transformation similar to theories of the Anthropocene today. The latter, writing in 1945, was already describing humans as a geological force. According to Foster, the contribution to environmental thinking made by scientists in the Soviet Union owed a lot to Karl Marx's dialectical and materialist understanding.[16]

For others on the left, however, the idea is unhelpful or even damaging for the goal of bringing about a more

13. Lewis, "A Force of Nature", as above.

14. See *www.underwatersculpture.com/sculptures/anthropocene/*

15. See John Bellamy Foster, "John Bellamy Foster Answers Three Questions on Marxism and Ecology", *La Revue du Projet*, 2016, *http://climateandcapitalism.com/2016/03/21/marxism-and-ecology-three-questions-for-john-bellamy-foster/* and Ian Angus, Facing the Anthropocene *(Monthly Review Press)*, 2016.

16. John Bellamy Foster, "Late Soviet Ecology and the Planetary Crisis", *Monthly Review*, volume 67, number 2, 2015.

environmentally just society. Naomi Klein has argued that using the term Anthropocene reduces the problem to one of human nature and lets capitalism off the hook.[17] For Andreas Malm the popularity of the idea "may be part of the problem" and he has called it "an indefensible abstraction at the point of departure".[18] This chapter summarises some of the debates among scientists, explains the criticisms from some on the left and concludes by arguing that, nevertheless, the idea remains useful and that Marxists should seek to use our existing tools to understand the phenomenon.

When did the Anthropocene begin?

Crutzen is a Nobel Prize winning atmospheric chemist famous for his work on the depletion of the ozone layer, while Stoermer is a freshwater biologist. But it is normally the task of geologists to decide when one epoch ends and another begins. Boundaries between geological time units represent major changes in the Earth System which have often involved rapid changes in the type of species on the planet as well as signatures in the rock strata. The start of the Cenozoic era 65 million years ago was marked by a dramatic loss of species including extinction for all the non-avian dinosaurs (the K-T extinction). It was the start of the era of birds and mammals. As well as changes in the fossil record, geologists prefer to find a marker of a specific event — known as a "golden spike" — in rock, sediment or glacier ice.[19] So a peak in the levels of the element iridium measured in the rocks at El Kef, Tunisia, is consistent with the idea that a meteor hit Earth at this time and provides an official geological marker for the Cenozoic.[20] The golden spike need not represent the

17. Naomi Klein, "Let Them Drown: The Violence of Othering in a Warming World", *London Review of Books*, volume 38, number 11, 2016, *www.lrb.co.uk/v38/n11/naomi-klein/let-them-drown*

18. Andreas Malm, *Fossil Capital* (Verso, 2016), pp32 and 391.

19. A golden spike can also be referred to as a GSSP (Global Stratotype Section and Point).

20. The actual impact took place not in Tunisia but in Mexico's Yucatán Peninsula.

most important thing that happened at the boundary between time periods, it simply serves as a marker that geologists can agree on.[21] Indeed, recent research suggests that the dinosaurs were already dying out, clearing the way for the evolution of mammals, and that the meteor strike itself was merely the final nail in the coffin.[22]

There has been much debate about when the Anthropocene started. One proposal is that the epoch actually began 11,700 years ago, which by convention we currently think of as the start of the Holocene (so Holocene could be renamed "Anthropocene" or geologists could keep the existing terminology and simply accept that the Holocene has been the real age of humans all along). The Holocene is when the last ice age ended; the relatively warm temperatures in the Northern hemisphere allowed human civilisations to spread throughout the globe and agriculture to develop.[23] Other proposals for an "early Anthropocene" push the start date back even further in time, to when humans caused the extinction of many large mammals or even to the first surviving evidence of any human activity.

There is some justification for dating the start of the Anthropocene back this far. The Holocene epoch was described in early geology manuals as the "anthropozoic" and the "age of mind and era of man".[24] An early Anthropocene start date would reflect the fact that the human species has always lived in a complex and developing relationship with our external environment, adapting our local environmental conditions to suit our needs throughout much of human history. We have been domesticating animals

21. Lewis and Maslin, "Defining the Anthropocene", as above.

22. Loulla-Mae Eleftheriou-Smith "Dinosaurs were 'in Decline' 50 Million Years Before Asteroid Strike Wiped Them Out, Study Suggests", *Independent*, 19 April 2016, *http://tinyurl.com/hnpqa7h*

23. The GSSP for this is a shift in the levels of deuterium in the Greenland ice core 11,700 years ago. This is evidence of global warming at the time.

24. Lewis and Maslin, "Defining the Anthropocene", as above.

and crop plants for thousands of years.[25] The development of agriculture in the Holocene influenced the way human societies have developed, allowing for the establishment of settlements and class and gender divisions within these societies. Judith Orr provides an overview of how human societies have developed in relationship with the environment with a particular emphasis on gender relations. She points out that, rather than being "a static backdrop to our lives", the environment "undergoes perpetual change and is also itself in part human-made".[26]

A contrasting proposal from Mark Maslin and Simon Lewis that teases out the role of colonialism in large-scale biospheric transformations, is that the Anthropocene started with the first contact with the "New World" by Europeans in 1492. Humans introduced New World crops such as maize and potatoes to Europe, Asia and Africa and transported wheat and sugarcane to the Americas causing significant changes to ecosystems that were irreversible, occurred all over the world and can be detected by, for example, the appearance of maize pollen in marine sediments off the coast of Italy. This period of history is referred to as "the Great Transformation" in Chris Harman's *A People's History of the World* as it was also the time of the renaissance and the associated "flowering of art and literature and scientific ideas".[27] But, as Harman also describes, the "discovery" and conquest of the New World brought slavery, famine and disease to many of the people living there. One Spanish observer described the effects on the Inca Empire: "infinite deserted villages on all the roads in the kingdom".[28] The human population of the Americas declined from an estimated 54 million to 6 million by 1650 and, with fewer people

25. Agriculture, and emissions from livestock and forest clearing, have had an effect on the planet's temperature from early in the Holocene and may have prevented global cooling that might otherwise have occurred — Jan Zalasiewicz, Mar Williams, Will Steffen, and Paul Crutzen, "The New World of the Anthropocene", *Environmental Science and Technology Viewpoint*, issue 44, 2010, *http://pubs.acs.org/doi/pdf/10.1021/es903118j*

26. Judith Orr, *Marxism and Women's Liberation* (Bookmarks, 2015), pp34-51.

27. Chris Harman, *A People's History of the World* (Bookmarks, 1999), p175.

28. Quoted in Harman, as above, p171.

to farm the land, forests started to return and levels of carbon dioxide in the atmosphere dipped. The drop in carbon dioxide level (it reached its lowest in 1610) could serve as a geological marker for this event as it can be detected in Antarctic ice.[29] The macabre hypothesis is that it may have been the deaths of millions of humans that marked the point when humanity became a significant global force.

While Lewis and Maslin's Orbis Spike proposal incorporates changes to ecosystems and human populations, Crutzen and Stoermer themselves focused more narrowly on energy use and greenhouse gas emissions. They initially suggested that the Anthropocene began towards the end of the 18th century. James Watt developed the steam engine in the 18th century and the first use of a coal fired steam engine to power a cotton mill was in Nottinghamshire in 1786.[30] This is also the time when, according to Crutzen and his colleagues, atmospheric greenhouse gas concentrations started to rise.[31] So, whereas for most of the Holocene levels of carbon dioxide in the atmosphere fluctuated — going up or down by up to 5ppm, since the industrial revolution, carbon dioxide levels have been rising by 2ppm per year.[32] Crutzen and Stoermer also propose a "great acceleration" around the middle of the 20th century — a "remarkable explosion" in which the levels of carbon dioxide in the atmosphere have begun to shoot up even more rapidly.[33]

Finally, some have proposed that the Anthropocene actually started in 1945.[34] The first nuclear weapons test (and the first

29. Lewis and Maslin, "Defining the Anthropocene" and *The Human Planet*, as above.

30. Malm, *Fossil Capital*, as above, p54.

31. Crutzen and Stoermer, "The 'Anthropocene'", as above.

32. Malm, *Fossil Capital,* as above.

33. Will Steffen, Paul Crutzen, and John McNeill, "The Anthropocene: Are Humans Now Overwhelming the Great Forces of Nature?", *Ambio: A Journal of the Human Environment*, volume 36, number 8, 2007. *www.pik-potsdam.de/news/public-events/archiv/alter-net/former-ss/2007/05-09.2007/steffen/literature/ambi-36-08-06_614_621.pdf*

34. Zalasiewicz and others, "When did the Anthropocene begin?", as above. The authors of this paper also seem to like the idea that the Anthropocene started with a bomb hitting Earth due the similarity of the event to the meteor strike that heralded the start of the Cenozoic.

usage of nuclear weapons in war) took place in this year and testing continued throughout the 1950s and 1960s, declining sharply after the Partial Test Ban Treaty in 1963. The effects of nuclear testing can be detected globally by measuring levels of radioactive isotopes in polar ice, lake sediments and tree rings. There is a clear peak in the levels of carbon isotopes from nuclear weapons in tree rings around this time that could act as a golden spike and it is absolutely unambiguous that this was caused by human activity.[35] This is, of course, extremely recent for geologists used to dealing with time periods of hundreds of thousands of years.[36]

Like the iridium deposits that mark the start of the Cenozoic, this does not mean that nuclear weapons testing was the most significant thing that happened at the time. To be considered the start date of the Anthropocene it would merely have to stand in to represent a time in which a profound shift in human societies and a related impact on planetary processes occurred. This is precisely what Earth System scientists are saying happened at around this time:

> The second half of the twentieth century is unique in the entire history of human existence on Earth. Many human activities reached take-off points sometime in the twentieth century and have accelerated sharply towards the end of the century. The last 50 years have without doubt seen the most rapid transformation of the human relationship with the natural world in the history of the species.[37]

35. Lewis and Maslin, "Defining the Anthropocene", as above.

36. It is standard practice in geology to refer to 1 January 1950 as "the present".

37. Will Steffen and others, *Global Change and the Earth System* (International Geosphere-Biosphere Programme, 2004), p258. *www.igbp.net/publications/igbpbookseries/ igbpbookseries/globalchangeandtheeearthsystem2004.5.1b8ae20512db692f2a680007462. html.* The time period of roughly 50 years ago is also consistent with the notion of a great acceleration although this is increasingly coming to be seen as the start of the Anthropocene epoch rather than a turning point within it.

Figure 1: Global real GDP, primary energy use and atmospheric carbon dioxide

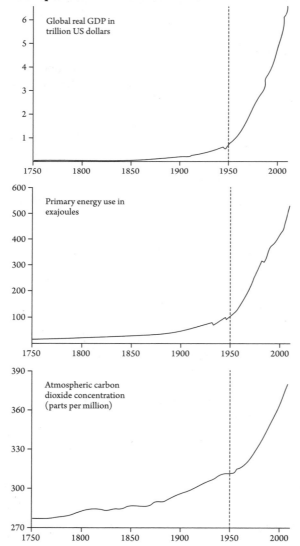

Source: Will Steffen, Wendy Broadgate, Lisa Deutsch, Owen Gaffney, and Cornelia Ludwig, "The Trajectory of the Anthropocene: The Great Acceleration", *Anthropocene Review,* 2015.

A 2015 paper by the Anthropocene Working Group — the group of scientists and others tasked with potentially adding the Anthropocene to the geological record — favoured a mid-20th century start date: "a pronounced, relatively sharp threshold in human modification of the global environment".[38] In summer 2016 the group's 35 members voted overwhelmingly that the Anthropocene is stratigraphically real and should be formalised. Furthermore, there were 28.3 votes for a start date around 1950, far more than for any other start date proposal such as the Orbis Spike and earlier potential start dates. Plutonium fallout was the most popular choice of primary signal.[39] Although the group do recognise that humans have left an impact on the stratigraphic record since before the start of the Holocene, the majority now agree that this influence intensified around the mid-20th century to such an extent that this point can be seen as the end of the Holocene.

The period since the Second World War has involved rapid population growth, urbanisation,[40] the intensification of agriculture and the widespread adoption of consumer goods such as televisions, cars and fridges. A marked increase in the adoption of disposable packaging at this time causing a huge waste problem is just one example of the environmental consequences of the shift.[41] Graphs of global GDP, energy use and carbon dioxide levels in the atmosphere is "hockey stick" shaped, showing a notable upturn around mid-century (figure 1, opposite).

Debates among geologists about when the Anthropocene began may seem far removed from, or even a distraction from, the more urgent task of dealing with climate change. However, differing views on when the Anthropocene began are often

38. Zalasiewicz and others, "When did the Anthropocene begin?", as above.

39. Anthropocene Working Group, "Media Note", 29 August 2016, *www2.le.ac.uk/ offices/press/press-releases/2016/august/media-note-anthropocene-working-group-awg (accessed online 29.7.18).*

40. The majority of people worldwide now live in cities.

41. Zalasiewicz and others, "When did the Anthropocene begin?", as above. On the politics behind disposable packaging and built in obsolescence in consumer goods see Martin Empson, *Land and Labour: Marxism, Ecology and Human History* (Bookmarks, 2014), chapter 11.

associated with very different interpretations of both its causes and potential solutions. Advocates of the various early Anthropocene hypotheses have been criticised for "normalising" global environmental change.[42] By arguing that the environmental problems of today have their roots in the emergence of human civilisation, early Anthropocene theorists play down the dangerous effects of climate change and the speed with which these environmental problems need to be addressed to avoid a catastrophe. This loses the power to shock and is one of the intriguing things about the Anthropocene diagnosis in the first place. Ian Angus supposes that these views are being promoted by anti-environmental lobbyists.[43]

Holocene conditions could hardly be described as benign. There have been disasters such as earthquakes, volcanoes, tsunamis and famines throughout the epoch. For much of the world's human population life has always been precarious. Nonetheless, the Holocene is often thought of as relatively conducive to human wellbeing compared to what the Anthropocene might bring: "Holocene conditions are the only ones that we know for sure are compatible with complex human societies".[44] Therefore, Angus prefers the idea that the Anthropocene started in the mid-20th century and refers to a global catastrophe with a very rapid onset that everyone should move quickly to address. So why are some on the left sceptical about discussions of the Anthropocene?

How not to talk about the Anthropocene

There is a particular narrative associated with the Anthropocene that is indeed highly problematic politically. The standard narrative goes something like this: there is something inherently destructive about humans; it is therefore inevitable that we have now reached the Anthropocene; all humans are

42. Lewis and Maslin, "Defining the Anthropocene", as above.

43. Ian Angus, "Hijacking the Anthropocene", *Climate and Capitalism,* 19 May 2015, *http://climateandcapitalism.com/2015/05/19/hijacking-the-anthropocene/*

44. Angus, "Entering the Age of Humans", as above.

implicated in this to some extent; as there is little we can do to change human nature we may need to take drastic measures (geoengineering) to fix the problem. For some proponents of the standard Anthropocene narrative, humanity's ability to use fire has led humans to manipulate the planet like no other species. When we figured out how to start fires in the distant past, it led in a linear progression to a situation where humans would at some point learn how to extract fossil fuels. We would inevitably end up burning those too. This kicked off a chain of events that led to a rapid expansion in fossil fuel use and the skyrocketing carbon emissions we can observe today. According to one scientific paper: "The mastery of fire by our ancestors provided humankind with a powerful monopolistic tool unavailable to other species that put us firmly on the long path towards the Anthropocene".[45]

This narrative involves a paradox. Humans seem to have more agency than we have ever had in the past. For the first time in human history we are able to push the whole planet into a new epoch. However, it is also assumed that we have very little agency actually to change the situation, faced as we are with the prospect of unleashing global forces that we have little power over except perhaps by unprecedented technological intervention.

Anthropocene scientists have referred to the "great forces" of nature, arguing that: "human activities have become so pervasive and profound that they rival the great forces of Nature".[46] This evokes the narcissistic notion that humanity is separate from the rest of nature and acts in opposition to it. In contemporary environmentalism, including in some discussions of the Anthropocene, this separation of nature from society is particularly problematic. It provides a philosophical

45. Steffen and others, "The Anthropocene: Are Humans Now Overwhelming the Great Forces of Nature?", as above. See Andreas Malm, "The Anthropocene Myth", *Jacobin*, 30 March 2015, *www.jacobinmag.com/2015/03/anthropocene-capitalism-climate-change/* for a critique of this thinking.

46. Steffen and others, "The Anthropocene: Are Humans Now Overwhelming the Great Forces of Nature?", as above.

underpinning to the notion that humans are nothing but an impact on "nature" and that the best thing we could do to "save nature" would be to scale back "our" impacts and try to leave the rest of the world alone. The standard narrative implies that "nature" was somehow pristine and unspoilt before human influence reached the levels that it presently has. Scientists have even stated that: "Earth has now left its natural geological epoch",[47] implying that there was something "natural" about the Holocene epoch. Recall that the Holocene itself only represents a very short period in geological terms, essentially a mere interval between ice ages, and that humans were already starting to influence the external environment during this time.

At the same time we are told we are overcoming the forces of nature, we are also a force of nature ourselves; human destructiveness is seen as somehow intrinsic to our own human "nature" so that the Anthropocene is simultaneously both a natural and an unnatural phenomenon.[48] By contrast a Marxist approach (of which more later) would need to proceed from a much more sophisticated, dialectical understanding of the role of humans within the natural world.

The dominant Anthropocene narrative has been criticised as post-political, with post-politics defined as "a socio-political arrangement that replaces ideological contestation and struggles by techno-managerial planning" and where "the space for political contestation, debate and reorientation is also restricted".[49] In other words, the narrative (as with some of the narratives around climate change more generally) tells us that we are all in it together. Precisely because climate change is viewed as a problem for the whole of humanity, we are told that we should put aside any differences of opinion over the

47. Steffen and others, "The Anthropocene: Are Humans Now Overwhelming the Great Forces of Nature?", as above.

48. Eva Lövbrand, Silke Beck, Jason Chilvers, Tim Forsyth, Johan Hedrén, Mike Hulme, Rolf Lidskog, and Eleftheria Vasileiadou, "Who Speaks for the Future of Earth? How Critical Social Science can Extend the Conversation on the Anthropocene", *Global Environmental Change,* volume 32, 2015 and Jason Moore, *Capitalism in the Web of Life* (Verso, 2015).

49. Lövbrand and others, "Who Speaks for the Future of Earth?", as above.

nature of the problem and work together to achieve a common solution. This tends to restrict political debate to very narrow questions around the type of technology to adopt.

Perhaps unsurprisingly then, Crutzen himself has suggested that high-tech geoengineering solutions might be needed to solve climate change. He has been sceptical about whether humans can get out of the climate situation quickly enough by political means and he favours a strategy of trying to cool the climate by firing sulphur into the air.[50] It is beyond the scope of this chapter to discuss the issue in full.[51] However, one criticism of this approach, as a technological solution to a problem caused by capitalist society, is that even if one of the various proposals were to actually work (by no means guaranteed), it would address the symptoms but not the ultimate cause of climate change. Cooling the planet down would not solve any of the other multiple environmental problems beyond global warming and would almost certainly have its own negative consequences. A more immediate concern is that, as climate scientist Kevin Anderson has pointed out, the promise of possible geoengineering fixes in the future can feed into political inaction today. The targets for greenhouse gas reduction set at the most UN talks in Paris in 2015 fell short of the radical action that is needed as they were premised on the idea that humanity would, at some point, come up with a way of sucking carbon dioxide out of the air. Although it is not Crutzen's intention, geoengineering may have gone from being a "last ditch Plan B" to part of the only plan.[52]

Related to the post-political narrative is the perverse idea that the Anthropocene is "good" or "great" and is something to be embraced. Erle Ellis points out that Homo sapiens is not the first species to have altered its external environment — when

50. Steve Connor, "Scientist Publishes 'Escape Route' from Global Warming", *Independent*, 30 July 2006, *http://tinyurl.com/dxe7w*

51. But see the various articles published by *Science for the People* in 2018 — *https://magazine.scienceforthepeople.org/tag/geoengineering/*

52. Kevin Anderson, "The Hidden Agenda: How Veiled Techno-utopias Shore up the Paris Agreement", 6 January 2016, *http://kevinanderson.info/blog/the-hidden-agenda-how-veiled-techno-utopias-shore-up-the-paris-agreement/*

green plants first evolved they changed the atmosphere dramatically by producing oxygen, for example. But humans are, unlike plants, conscious of the effect we have on the rest of the planet and able to change our actions. This is a reasonable point to make, but for Ellis it comes tied to the idea that we have finally "woken up" to the negative effects we are having and just need to put the knowledge that we are in the Anthropocene to good use:

> The boom in Anthropocene discussions might itself indicate that societies are waking up to the realities of becoming a global force in the Earth system...we might guide this new "great force of nature" toward better outcomes for both humanity and nonhuman nature. It is time to embrace what makes us human, ultrasociality, and turn it towards the grand challenges of the Anthropocene — to intentionally build better societies and cultures of nature.[53]

Advocates of the idea of a good Anthropocene have described it as a great opportunity to offer an "optimistic vision" of a future society founded on increased use of technology. They have even criticised mainstream environmentalists as being too pessimistic in raising concerns about natural disasters or resource depletion. Again, there seems to be little discussion of who will be responsible for implementing all the proposed technological innovations.[54]

However, not everyone who uses the term Anthropocene has adopted the dualistic thinking of the standard narrative. For some commentators, rather than demonstrating the human impact on nature, the Anthropocene idea is useful precisely because it forces us to acknowledge how closely entangled human activity is with the rest of nature. After all, every terrestrial living thing lives in an environment that has a higher concentration of

53. Ellis, "Evolving toward a better Anthropocene", as above.
54. Angus, "Hijacking the Anthropocene", as above.

greenhouse gases in it than it would without humans. Therefore, the Anthropocene idea could also make a contribution to a body of work within the social sciences that has always criticised the concept of "nature" as something separate from human society. One example of such an approach — although not written from a Marxist perspective — is Jamie Lorimer's book *Wildlife in the Anthropocene*, which uses the idea of the Anthropocene to draw attention to the wildlife that lives in human created environments such as cities, therefore criticising the association of nature with "wilderness".[55]

An Anthropocene myth?

One prominent critic of the Anthropocene narrative from a left-wing perspective is Andreas Malm. Malm is an academic and an activist who is rightly strongly critical of the lack of action by delegates at the Paris talks in 2015. He calls for "militant resistance on the streets" to confront climate change.[56] Clearly he is far from complacent about the scale of today's environmental problems. So why has he referred to the "Anthropocene Myth"?

In his critique of these ideas Malm returns to Crutzen's suggestion that the Anthropocene began with the invention of the steam engine, the industrial revolution and the associated increase in fossil fuel use. He offers an important counter-narrative to the idea that this was a direct result of humankind's earlier mastery of fire, pointing out that Crutzen and others do not say a lot about what actually caused the adoption of steam power in Britain around the 1830s. Basing his arguments on a detailed historical analysis, he shows how the rise of the steam engine came about in a capitalist society and served a particular purpose at the time.

Malm argues that steam engines were not technologically superior to alternative forms of technology such as the water

55. Jamie Lorimer, *Wildlife in the Anthropocene: Conservation after Nature* (University of Minnesota Press, 2015).

56. Andreas Malm, "Our Fight for Survival", *Jacobin*, 29 November 2015, *www.jacobinmag.com/2015/11/climate-change-paris-cop21-hollande-united-nations/*

wheel, either in the amount of energy that could be produced or how cheaply it could be produced. In fact for an individual factory owner buying coal was the more expensive option. However, coal did offer several other advantages for the capitalist: It provided a regular supply of energy; it didn't require different capitals to band together and invest in infrastructure in the way that water did; it could be used at a convenient time of day; and perhaps most notably, steam power brought industrial production into cities such as Manchester. Cities increasingly provided a plentiful supply of cheap and exploitable labour power.[57] Note that, for Malm, steam power was "presupposed" by an early capitalist system in which a small minority owned the means of production and much of the rest of society were being drawn into wage labour:

> While it is admittedly banal to point out, steam engines were not adopted by some natural-born deputies of the human species. The choice of a prime mover in commodity production could not possibly have been the prerogative of that species, since it presupposed, for a start, the institution of wage labour. It was the owners of the means of production who installed the novel prime mover.[58]

Central to this argument is the idea that climate change is political, and the adoption of coal came about as a result of class struggle.[59] The Anthropocene was brought about consciously, not in the sense that capitalists then understood or predicted climate change, but nevertheless they did take concerted action, in the face of fierce resistance, to shift to burning fossil fuels. It didn't just happen as part of some natural process of

57. Malm, *Fossil Capital*, as above, and Martin Empson's review, "Why Capitalism is Addicted to Oil and Coal", *Climate and Capitalism*, 17 December 2015, *http://climateandcapitalism. com/2015/12/17/fossil-capital-the-rise-of-steam-power-and-the-roots-of-global-warming/*

58. Malm, "The Anthropocene Myth", as above.

59. See also Amy Leather's article on fossil fuels in this book.

human evolution.

Another point that follows from Malm's general line of argument is that, of course, we as the human race are not all equally responsible for the burning of fossil fuels. The shift to such a system was brought about by a particular subset of the human species in the 19th century: wealthy, white, British and male. To this day the responsibility for carbon emissions cannot possibly be said to lie with humanity as a whole. A person's individual energy consumption depends to an overwhelming extent on the type of society they live in. The energy consumption of an average Canadian is a staggering 1,000 times greater than that of a typical farmer in the Sahel. Overall, the poorest 45 percent of humanity generate just 7 percent of the carbon emissions.[60]

It is worth noting here that Malm's argument is not necessarily a critique of the word Anthropocene per se. What he objects to is a particular narrative associated with its use.[61] But equally it is fair to say that he is sceptical about how useful it would be for Marxists to take up the term Anthropocene.

There is much to agree with in Malm's arguments. It makes sense to try to politicise climate change and to point the finger at the capitalists rather than the "Anthropos" or humanity in general. The environment could once again become a site of class struggle. People are starting to engage in climate activism in greater numbers, most recently with the growth of groups like Extinction Rebellion and the extraordinary global school strikes. For many, radical slogans such as "system change, not climate change" make sense. Struggles over climate jobs, where trade unionists and others demand jobs that could cut emissions, over the local environmental consequences of resource extraction (fracking, tar sands extraction, gold mining, etc) and over the impacts of the extreme weather events all start to raise

60. Malm, *Fossil Capital*, p269 and Andreas Malm and Alf Hornborg, "The Geology of Mankind? A Critique of the Anthropocene Narrative", Anthropocene Review, volume 1, number 1, 2014.

61. Malm made this point at a book launch for *Fossil Capital* in London on 2 March 2016.

the issue that when it comes to climate change we are not "all in it together".[62]

However, several commentators, including Marxists, have argued against dismissing the notion of the Anthropocene. Much of Malm's argument hangs on a critique of Crutzen and of a few others with particularly problematic views. But the debates around the Anthropocene are becoming much wider than that. It seems premature to associate the Anthropocene so closely with the industrial revolution especially as the Anthropocene Working Group prefer a more recent start date. Also, in fairness to these scientists they are aware that not all humans are equally to blame for climate change. Crutzen himself has argued from early on that only 25 percent of humans are responsible.[63] After receiving some criticisms from social scientists, further work has been produced that differentiates between humans at least based on whether they live in rich or poor countries, although this is not the same as a historical and class analysis of the ultimate roots of the problem.[64]

Malm tends towards explaining historical developments in terms of class struggle between one group of humans and another where the most powerful group will win out (an approach that could be described as class struggle determinism). This examination of what happens between humans gives very little emphasis to the way human societies develop in a relationship with the rest of nature. Jason W Moore has sharply criticised this type of thinking, pointing out that "human activity not only produces biospheric change, but relations between humans are themselves produced by nature".[65] Moore consequently argues

62. See Suzanne Jeffery's chapter in this book.

63. Paul Crutzen, "Geology of Mankind", *Nature*, volume 415, 2002, *www.geo.utexas.edu/courses/387h/PAPERS/Crutzen2002.pdf*

64. Will Steffen, Wendy Broadgate, Lisa Deutsch, Owen Gaffney, and Cornelia Ludwig, "The Trajectory of the Anthropocene: The Great Acceleration", *Anthropocene Review*, 2015, *https://favaretoufabc.files.wordpress.com/2013/06/2015-steffen-et-al-the-great-acceleration-1.pd*f

65. Jason W Moore, "The Capitalocene, Part I: On the Nature and Origins of our Ecological Crisis", *Journal of Peasant Studies*, volume 44, issue 3, 2017. See also Moore, *Capitalism in the Web of Life*, as above.

that the origins of the epoch should be traced to profound shifts in socio-natural relations beginning as far back as the late 15th century with the origins of the capitalist system rather than with the 19th century expansion in fossil fuel use.

For many, the Anthropocene gives a name to a phenomenon that is actually happening in reality and for which the scientific evidence is overwhelming. What is therefore needed is an understanding of the causes of the Anthropocene rather than a rejection of the word itself. It has also, to some extent, started a discussion among scientists, activists and members of the public about the environment and humanity's role within it which is surely to be welcomed.

Towards a Marxist approach

To understand the Anthropocene requires an approach that studies the earth as a complex system in which living things, including humans organised in societies, play an active role. To quote Will Steffen and others:

> Crucial to the emergence of this perspective has been the dawning awareness of two aspects of Earth System functioning. First that the earth itself is a single system within which the biosphere is an active, essential component. Secondly, that human activities are now so pervasive and profound in their consequences that they affect the earth at a global scale in complex, interactive and apparently accelerating ways.[66]

Making sense of this system will need ideas from both the social and the natural sciences. And it will require an interpretation of how a complex system can undergo change gradually or abruptly. It is entirely possible to argue that humans have always existed in a complex relationship with our environments but also that there have been recent and decisive shifts in the nature of

66. Steffen and others, *Global Change and the Earth System*, as above, p1.

this relationship and therefore to take the recent Anthropocene proposals seriously. None of this is alien to Marxist thought. In fact, the approach outlined by Karl Marx and Friedrich Engels to humanity's role within the natural world and subsequently developed by more recent generations of Marxists offers a sophisticated basis on which to assess the implications of the Anthropocene.

Ellis argues that the Anthropocene requires us to understand why humans, rather than any other species, became a global force. How and why did we go from hunting and gathering to living in agricultural societies and, later, more complex societies with cities, diverse job roles and rapidly developing technology? How did we reach the point where we are changing the natural world so profoundly that our influence can be measured in the geological record?[67] These are questions that Marxism can play a role in answering. Marx begins his own analysis of the labour process in *Capital* by pointing out that humans act on external nature but at the same time also change themselves. It seems he would have agreed on the point that humans have differentiated ourselves from other animals in our ability to transform the rest of the world. He famously argued that:

> A spider conducts operations which resemble those of a weaver, and a bee would put many a human architect to shame by the construction of its honeycomb cells. But what distinguishes the worst architect from the best of bees is that the architect builds the cell in his mind before he constructs it in wax.[68]

So, humans are able to manipulate the natural world with a qualitatively greater capacity for conscious and intentional action than other animals (although we are not all-powerful, our actions can also have unforeseen and unintended consequences).

Humans evolved from the same ancestors as other animals

67. Ellis, "Evolving toward a better Anthropocene", as above.
68. Karl Marx, *Capital*, volume 1 (Penguin Classics, 1990), p284.

so our differentiated abilities cannot have been innate but must have arisen in a process of evolution; Engels offered one hypothesis as to how human capacities evolved from those of our primate ancestors in his short essay "The Part Played By Labour In The Transition From Ape To Man".[69] This transition, he supposed, took place as a result of our ancestors' manipulation of the external environment mediated by labour. As he concludes:

> All the planned action of all animals has never succeeded in impressing the stamp of their will upon the earth. That was left for man. In short, the animal merely uses its environment, and brings about changes in it simply by its presence; man by his changes makes it serve his ends, masters it. This is the final, essential distinction between man and other animals, and once again it is labour that brings about this distinction.[70]

The transition "from ape to man" represented a qualitative shift in the ways in which humans related to external nature. So Marx and Engels had already laid the basis for an understanding of the ways in which a further shift might have taken place as we pushed planetary conditions from Holocene to Anthropocene.

Marx's point that we change our nature as we adapt external nature is also a starting point for a much more sophisticated understanding of human nature than the simplistic approach associated with some interpretations of the Anthropocene. All humans share basic needs due to our biology such as the need for food, water, sleep and shelter, etc; we can criticise capitalism on the basis that it cannot adequately provide for our needs. But there is no reason to suggest that we have always been individualistic, violent or competitive. Rather "our nature is in a constant

69. Friedrich Engels, *The Part Played by Labour in the Transition from Ape to Man* (Progress Publishers, 1934 [1876]). *www.marxists.org/archive/marx/works/1876/part-played-labour/*
70. Engels, as above.

process of evolution".[71] Our behaviour and psychology have changed dramatically throughout history as we have lived in different types of society. For Marx there is no essential "human essence" that can be abstracted from social relations.[72]

As some are arguing that there is something innate in humans that compels us to burn fossil fuels, Marxist understandings of human nature and how it developed in line with the needs of different types of society are clearly relevant here. Indeed, the idea of a fixed and inherently destructive human nature that is responsible for environmental problems has been effectively criticised. For example, in an article on biodiversity conservation Ian Rappel locates the origins of this misanthropic thinking in biological determinism, which suggests that our apparent tendency towards destructive behaviour can be explained by our genetic make-up.[73]

Human action involves a complex relationship with the natural world but we do not relate to it just as individuals. We are also social beings whose relationship with nature varies with the type of society we live in. Recognising this basic point is central to the approach to environmental issues developed by writers in this journal and elsewhere. It allows us to show how environmental problems arose as societies changed throughout history and serves as a basis on which to study the specific ways in which capitalism is damaging. It also means we can envision a future socialist society where a more rational approach to the environment will correspond to more democratic and egalitarian social relations.[74]

Although human societies involve a relationship with the

71. Paul Blackledge, "How Humans Make Themselves", *International Socialism* 117, winter 2007, http://isj.org.uk/how-humans-make-themselves/

72. Blackledge, as above; Elizabeth Terzakis, "What do Socialists say about Human Nature?", *International Socialist Review*, issue 47, May-June 2006, *www.isreview.org/issues/47/wdss-humnature.shtml*

73. Ian Rappel, "Capitalism and Species Extinction", *International Socialism* 147, summer 2015, http://isj.org.uk/capitalism-and-species-extinction/

74. Empson, *Land and Labour* and Martin Empson, "Can we Build a Sustainable Society?", *Socialist Review*, December 2015, *http://socialistreview.org.uk/408/can-we-build-sustainable-society*

environment, capitalism differs from previous societies in its detrimental effects. Whereas feudal lords, for example, would exploit the peasants and serfs, they only needed to do so to satisfy their own material needs and those of their entourage. In a capitalist society individual capitalists are compelled to compete against each other to accumulate more surplus value by exploiting their workforce. If a capitalist fails to extract surplus value and invest it in further production they risk going out of business.[75] Klein explains how this happens in the contemporary fossil fuels industry. Companies that do not have access to oil and gas reserves to meet expected future demand lose out as their investors put their money elsewhere and are therefore forced to search the globe for more places where they can drill.[76] This constant drive towards accumulation turns more and more of the natural world into commodities that can be used. As Moore describes, as capitalism entrenched itself globally from the mid-15th century onwards it stalked the earth in search of more commodities, such as iron, silver, timber and sugar, cutting down forests at a rapid rate as it went.[77] The development of capitalism has therefore gone hand in hand with a huge expansion in the forces of production — the technology, resources, practices and knowledge available for use in the production process.[78]

Angus agrees that the problem is capitalism, but says that we should seek to understand the environmental implications of a specific development within capitalism after the Second World War, the advent of monopoly capital. The increasing domination of large monopolies limits competition as small firms are denied access to the market. It leads to the creation of an excess surplus for which there are not enough productive outlets for companies to invest in.[79] Angus also adds that, rather than just being a marker of the divide between the early

75. Empson, *Land and Labour*, as above, chapter 11.

76. Naomi Klein, *This Changes Everything: Capitalism vs the Climate* (Penguin, 2015).

77. Moore, *Capitalism in the Web of Life* and "The Capitalocene", as above.

78. Empson, *Land and Labour*, as above, chapter 11.

79. Angus, "The Anthropocene: When did it begin and why does it matter?", as above.

20th century and the late 20th century, the Second World War itself was significant to the social changes that came after it. He points out that the war left the United States in a much more advantageous economic position compared to European states, that manufacturing technology was revolutionised during the war and that state investment in armaments and manufacturing more generally continued after the war benefitting US monopolies in particular.[80] The monopoly capital approach has been criticised for over-emphasising economic stagnation in the US and downplaying the role competition plays in Marxist analysis.[81] As outlined above, competition and the search for profits are the ultimate driving forces behind capitalism's destructive ecological role rather than stagnation and monopoly. However, Angus makes a more general point: socialists should analyse the specific ways in which capitalism has changed during the 20th century as well as the workings of the system in the abstract.

Marxists have also argued that, rather than simply "acting on" nature, capitalism can be said to reorganise nature. For example, Rappel also describes the creation of a "capitalist ecology" with its own distinctive characteristics including a tendency towards growing crops in monocultures, exhausting supplies of resources and discharging waste into the environment as pollution: "The ecology that is actively engineered under capitalism is one determined by ruling class aspirations for profit".[82] If Marxists accept that capitalism constructs a particular ecology, it is not much of a leap to suggest that we are in the Anthropocene. In other words, capitalism has allowed the construction of a particular ecology on a global scale and to the extent that the effects of this can now be understood in terms of a shift from one geological epoch to another.

If the Anthropocene started in the last few centuries, or even as recently as the middle of the 20th century, it must have

80. Angus, *Facing the Anthropocene*, as above, pp137-145.

81. Joseph Choonara, "Marxist Accounts of the Current Crisis", *International Socialism* 123, summer 2009, *http://isj.org.uk/marxist-accounts-of-the-current-crisis/*

82. Rappel, "Capitalism and Species Extinction", as above, p110.

arisen due to the influence of capitalism throughout the world. Humans have lived in many types of society, but only capitalism has given rise to the Anthropocene. Some have suggested that if environmental problems can be located with capitalism not humanity, "Capitalocene" might be a better word to use.[83] This terminology may yet become more popular, especially among radical social scientists. However, one disadvantage is that it is less likely to be accepted by geologists and other physical scientists (it doesn't fit with the conventions of geological terminology) as well as those who are concerned about the environment but who don't (or don't yet) blame capitalism.[84] As the word "Anthropocene" has already entered common usage it may simply be too late to start proposing alternative terms.

Malm argues that discussions of the Anthropocene have been dominated by natural scientists. Writing with Alf Hornborg he has called it "the illogical and ultimately self-defeating foray of the natural science community...into the domain of human affairs". The authors argue that such people "extend their world-views to society" and that "geologists, meteorologists and their colleagues are not necessarily well-equipped to study the sort of things that take place between humans".[85] The argument that follows is that understanding the social reasons for the growth of fossil fuel use for instance should be left to historians and other social scientists. But Marx and Engels themselves would not have been so dismissive of scientific insights or claimed that natural scientists are stepping out of line if they comment on issues that involve humans. Both took an interest in the scientific discoveries of their own time, particularly Darwin's theories of evolution. This is not to say that they were uncritical of Darwin's views, which were often rooted in liberal ideology, but they did see how the kernel of his thinking could be important to the development of their own worldview. In this spirit Angus calls for a synthesis

83. For example, Moore, "The Capitalocene", as above.
84. Angus, *Facing the Anthropocene,* as above, pp230-231.
85. Malm and Hornborg, "The Geology of Mankind?", as above.

of insights from Earth System science and ecological Marxism. He complains about "carping from the sidelines about the scientists' lack of social analysis" and argues that instead socialists should pay much more attention to what the physical scientists are saying: "ecosocialists need to approach the Anthropocene project as an opportunity to unite an ecological Marxist analysis with the latest scientific research, in a new synthesis — a socio-ecological account of the origins, nature, and direction of the current crisis in the Earth System".[86]

There is a danger in accepting uncritically the ideas and the narratives coming from some quarters and especially from the super-optimistic "let's not let a good crisis go to waste" purveyors of the "good Anthropocene" argument. But there are plenty of situations, including climate change itself, where we might not agree with the dominant narrative about the ultimate cause of a problem or the solutions proposed by the ruling class, but where we would agree that the problem exists. If some scientists have ideas that we might find problematic, this isn't helped by socialists dismissing the whole notion of the Anthropocene — effectively leaving the argument in the hands of the right.[87]

Scientists are now telling us that "business as usual...is not a viable option".[88] If capitalism is allowed to continue, the extinction of humanity is an all too real possibility. In that case the Anthropocene is unlikely to last long and will register as a short geological episode. The alternative is that we can overthrow capitalism and replace it with a sustainable society, one that allows our species to continue.

***

86. Angus, "The Anthropocene: When did it begin and why does it matter?", as above.
87. Angus, "Entering the Age of Humans", as above.
88. Will Steffen endorsement for Angus, *Facing the Anthropocene*, as above.

Chapter 3

The Discovery and Rediscovery of Metabolic Rift

Ian Angus

> Modern bourgeois society, with its relations of produc-
> tion, of exchange and of property, a society that has
> conjured up such gigantic means of production and of
> exchange, is like the sorcerer who is no longer able to
> control the powers of the nether world whom he has
> called up by his spells. — Karl Marx and Frederick Engels

Global warming. Superstorms. Rising sea levels. Toxic air and
smog. Ocean acidification and dead zones. Species extinction. Soil
erosion. Fresh water depletion. Ozone destruction. Indestruct-
ible plastics and chemical pollution. Deforestation. Expanding
deserts. Antibiotic resistant bacteria. New diseases and plagues.

The list goes on.

We face a planetary emergency, a convergence of ecological
crises that threatens the survival of civilisation.

In 2009, a group of 28 internationally renowned scientists,
convened by the Stockholm Resilience Centre, identified nine
planetary boundaries that define what they call "a safe operating

space for humanity." Crossing any one of those thresholds, they wrote, could have deleterious or even disastrous consequences for human well-being. An update published in 2015 showed that seven of the nine critical planetary boundaries are close to or already in the danger zone.[1]

That research, and much more like it, leads irresistibly to the conclusion that modest reforms and policy shifts will not prevent environmental catastrophe. What we confront are not individual problems that can be tackled one at a time, but an interlocked set of disruptions of the fundamental natural processes that have made Earth habitable for thousands of years.

Something has gone terribly wrong in the relationship between human society and the earth. Addressing symptoms alone is dangerous: a fix for one problem may make others worse. Radical remedies are obviously required, but we won't find a cure unless we identify the underlying cause, the systemic disease that is attacking our life-support systems.

Marxism and nature

Most explanations of the complex relationship between human society and the natural world fall into one of two broad categories — dualist accounts that view humans and society as separate from nature, and monist accounts that view them as a single integrated identity. Many environmental writers attribute environmental destruction to the idea of dualism: if humans would only realize that they are part of nature they would not treat it so badly. In one version of that argument, we can only build sustainable societies if we abandon our human-centred anthropocentric outlook and adopt nature-centred ecocentric views.

A recent variant argues that while nature and society may once have been separate entities, capitalism and society are

1. Stockholm Resilience Centre, "The nine planetary boundaries", *https://www. stockholmresilience.org/research/planetary-boundaries/planetary-boundaries/about-the-research/the-nine-planetary-boundaries.html*

now entirely enclosed within each other, and any other view is a dualist and bourgeois illusion.

As environmental philosopher Richard Evanoff points out, "this monism collapses...once it is recognised that while all human artefacts are indeed constructed by nature, not all that can be called nature is constituted by human artefacts." Much of nature is beyond human management and control, and while nature constrains human society in many ways, it does not determine what society must be like. Evanoff argues instead for a dialectical approach.

> The dialectical approach is neither dualistic nor monistic... While humans both constitute and are constituted by the natural environment, they neither constitute nor are constituted by the *whole* natural environment. Similarly, while the built environment both constitutes and is constituted by the natural environment, it neither constitutes nor is constituted by the whole natural environment.[2]

That dialectical approach is fundamental to Marxism. Marx and Engels viewed humans as part of and dependent upon the rest of the natural world, not because they had a monist philosophy, but because they began from the undeniable fact that we cannot do anything at all, we cannot even exist, unless we obtain food, air, water and other essentials from the world around us. Nature, Marx wrote, is "man's inorganic body" — that is, an essential part of us that is not contained in our biological organs. "Man lives from nature, ie nature is his body, and he must maintain a continuing dialogue with it if he is not to die."[3]

Because we are physical beings, we always have depended and always will depend on exchanges of matter and energy with the rest of the natural world. Scientists in Marx's day used

2. Richard J Evanoff, "Reconciling Realism and Constructivism in Environmental Ethics," *Environmental Values*, vol 14, no 1, 2005, p74. Emphasis in original.

3. Karl Marx, *Early Writings* (Penguin, 1974), p328

the German word stoffwechsel for those essential exchanges — the English equivalent is metabolism.

That mutual dependence is the first principle of historical materialism, but if we stop there, we miss the next principle, that the ways in which humans obtain the necessities of life from nature have changed through history. In order to understand the specific relationship between any particular social order and the natural world, we must look beyond humans as physical beings and examine the concrete social circumstances in which they produce and reproduce. As Marx wrote, that's particularly important with capitalist society, which has separated most humans from the natural world they depend upon.

> It is not the *unity* of living and active humanity with the natural, inorganic conditions of their metabolic exchange with nature, and hence their appropriation of nature, which requires explanation or is the result of a historic process, but rather the separation between these inorganic conditions of human existence and this active existence, a separation which is completely posited only in the relation of wage-labour and capital.[4]

As Marx showed long ago, capitalism subordinates the satisfaction of human needs to its inherent drive for profit and wealth accumulation. In the process, it "disrupts the metabolic interaction between man and the earth," and generates "an irreparable rift in the interdependent process of social metabolism, a metabolism prescribed by the natural laws of life itself".[5]

Like an anti-immune disease that attacks the body it dwells in, capitalism is both part of the natural world and at war with it. It simultaneously depends upon and undermines its life support systems.

4. Karl Marx, *Grundrisse: Foundations of the Critique of Political Economy* (Rough Draft), Martin Nicolaus trans. (Penguin, 1973), p489. Emphasis in original.

5. Karl Marx, *Capital; A Critique of Political Economy, vol 1*. Ben Fowkes trans. (Penguin, 1976), pp949-50.

That insight is the basis of metabolic rift theory, which, as the late Del Weston argued, is "the crux of Marx's ecological critique of capitalism, denoting the disjuncture between social systems and the rest of nature."

> The metabolic rift… refers to a rupture in the metabolism of the whole ecological system, including humans' part in that system. The concept is built around how the logic of accumulation severs basic processes of natural reproduction, leading to the deterioration of the environment and ecological sustainability and disrupting the basic operations of nature. It neatly captures the lack of balance between 'expenditure and income' in the earth's metabolism under the capitalist system.[6]

Marx's concept of a metabolic rift in agriculture was based on the work of chemist Justus von Liebig, who showed that English agricultural and social practices were depleting the soil of essential nutrients, forcing farmers to use ever-increasing amounts of artificial fertilizers and imported guano. That particular metabolic rift has continued to grow, and it has been joined by many other ruptures in the basic processes of the Earth System.

> This rift has grown both in dimensions and complexity, to the point where the economic activities of human society are causing an unprecedented change in the earth's biosphere, its lands, forests, water and air, potentially bringing to an end the Holocene era as a result of anthropogenic global warming.[7]

Frederick Engels wrote that the essential characteristic of all living organisms is "continual metabolic interchange with

6. Del Weston, *The Political Economy of Global Warming: the Terminal Crisis* (Routledge, 2014), p67.

7. Weston, *The Political Economy of Global Warming*, as above, p66.

the natural environment outside them".[8] The history of life on Earth, and thus of humanity, is ultimately the history of the changing ways in which living things have obtained, processed and exchanged matter and energy. It is a history of metabolism, the fundamental prerequisite of all life. Four billion years of evolution have produced innumerable species and life-webs that are metabolically connected at every level, from the smallest cell to the entire planet.

Grasping that principle is an essential first step towards understanding the relationship between society and the rest of nature, and of the ecological crises that result when human activity, mediated through the most destructive social order that has ever existed, disrupts the metabolic cycles on which all life depends.

Socialism versus the environment?
One of Marx's strongest statements on what the relationship between humanity and the rest of nature ought to be appears in his masterwork, *Capital*:

> From the standpoint of a higher socioeconomic forma-
> tion, the private property of particular individuals in the
> earth will appear just as absurd as the private property
> of one man in other men. Even an entire society, a nation,
> or all simultaneously existing societies taken together,
> are not the owners of the earth. They are simply its
> possessors, its beneficiaries, and have to bequeath it
> in an improved state to succeeding generations as boni
> patres familias [good heads of the household].[9]

In the 1870s, Karl Marx, exasperated by the actions of some

8. Frederick Engels, *Dialectics of Nature* (International Publishers, 1940), pp195-7.

9. Karl Marx, *Capital: A Critique of Political Economy, vol 3,* David Fernbach trans. (Penguin, 1981), p911. In another translation, the word "beneficiaries" is rendered as usufructories, a legal concept under which a person has a right to use property owned by another but must keep it in good condition.

of his French followers, commented, "All I know is that I am not a Marxist." If he had lived through the 20th century, he would undoubtedly have said the same about the environmental policies of regimes that claimed to be his political heirs. Good heads of households they were not!

To take just one example, in the 1960s Soviet authorities launched a massive river-diversion project in Kazakhstan, Uzbekistan, and Turkmenistan, to irrigate new cotton plantations. The plantations bloomed and the USSR quickly became the second-largest cotton exporter in the world, but the region as a whole suffered unprecedented ecological disaster. The diverted rivers had fed the Aral Sea, which was the fourth-largest lake in the world, the size of Lake Huron. By 1989 it had shrunk by 90 percent, the remaining water was heavily polluted, drinking water was fouled, nearby farms were destroyed by blowing salt, and a once vibrant fishing industry was gone.[10]

A collateral result of the many environmental disasters in the former Soviet Union and China, and of the willingness of many socialists in the west to ignore or even defend such destructive projects, has been that many environmentalists have rejected Marxism. They have seen socialism and capitalism as anti-environmental twins, and have sought a third road, derived in some way from ecological science. "Neither left nor right, but out front," became a popular slogan for green parties in the 1980s, and in the 1990s a number of attempts were made to develop "ecologism" as a new approach to politics.

Many articles and books by greens featured (and still do) a search for socialism's anti-environmental original sin in the writings of Marx and Engels. Most commonly, the founders of modern socialism are accused of productivism — the view that ever-expanding production of material goods is an unalloyed good — and of failing to understand the value of nature. Such criticisms reflect a profound misunderstanding of what Marx and Engels wrote and believed, but they have been

10. Murray Feshbach and Alfred Friendly, *Ecocide in the USSR: Health and Nature under Siege* (Basic Books, 1993), pp73-75.

widely accepted in green circles, justifying outright rejection of socialism in general and Marxism in particular.

It must be said that prior to the 1990s, Marxists did very little to correct green misunderstandings, or to develop their own understanding of the growing environmental crisis using Marx's methods. With few exceptions, socialist movements in the 20th century either ignored environmental issues or blithely deferred all consideration of the subject until after the revolution, when socialism would magically solve them all.

During the first wave of modern environmentalism in the 1970s, some individual socialists tried to make the case that Marxism, properly understood, offered a valuable methodology for understanding and responding to the growing environmental crisis. For example, in 1970 István Mészáros devoted a significant part of his Deutscher Memorial Prize lecture to "Capitalism and ecological destruction," and in 1972 the Detroit-based radical lawyer Ronald Reosti published "Pollution: Who is responsible?" an insightful essay that unfortunately wasn't widely read.[11]

But those were exceptions. While socialist publications often used accounts of pollution to illustrate capitalism's failures, they didn't offer a coherent analysis of environmental issues, and most organised Marxist groups stood aside from efforts to build environmental campaigns and protests.[12]

I don't suggest that if Marxists had done a better job at

11. Mészáros's 1970 lecture is available in many editions, but most readily in Istvan Mészáros, *The Necessity of Social Control* (Monthly Review, 2015), pp23-51. Reosti's essay was published in Stephanie Coontz, ed, *Life in Capitalist America: Private Profit and Social Decay* (Pathfinder, 1975), pp227-242.

12. This abstention wasn't limited to any specific political current. Barry Sheppard's detailed history of the US Socialist Workers Party, a Trotskyist group that was active in anti-war, women's liberation and other movements, mentions ecology only in regard to articles in a party newspaper, and doesn't mention participating in the environmental movement. See Barry Sheppard, *The Party: the Socialist Workers Party, 1960-1988.* Vol. 1 (Resistance Books, 2005), p251. Max Elbaum's history of Maoism in the US says that groups in that current viewed environmentalism as "a backward distraction from the class struggle," and as a result "were unable...to appreciate the significance of one of the most crucial issues and vital movements of the 1970s and beyond." Max Elbaum, *Revolution in the Air: Sixties Radicals Turn to Lenin, Mao and Che* (Verso, 2018), p139. *Monthly Review*, the most widely-read Marxist journal in the US since 1949, and now a major voice for ecosocialism, carried only eight articles on environmental issues in the first 40 years of its existence.

this, then the environmental movement would have been more radical and ecosocialism would have emerged earlier. From the early 1980s to the end of the century, the Marxist left was battered by the rise of neoliberalism and the ignominious collapse of "really existing socialism" in the USSR and Eastern Europe. As a result, it was in no position to influence the environmental movement, which in any event had moved to the right, tacitly adopting the view, concisely expressed by Margaret Thatcher, that there is no alternative to capitalism.

Still, the failure of Marxists to make their own case contributed to the outright rejection of Marxism, even among radical greens.

Hybrid ecosocialism

The word ecosocialism originated in Germany as *ökosozialismus* in the late 1970s, and made its first English language appearance in *Eco-Socialism in a Nutshell*, a pamphlet published in England in 1980.[13] In both cases the term referred to an eclectic mix of social-democratic and environmental reforms, not to a coherent red-green worldview or to Marxism in any form.

It wasn't until 1989 that serious discussions of Marxism and environmentalism took off, with the launch of the academic journal *Capitalism Nature Socialism*. Its early years were particularly notable for wide-ranging discussions of editor James O'Connor's "second contradiction of capitalism" thesis, that capitalism's anti-ecological tendencies would undermine profits and cause economic crises.[14] CNS began calling itself a "journal of ecosocialism" in 2007, but recently its editorial emphasis has tilted towards anarchism. Unfortunately, high subscription prices and an Internet paywall have

13. The authoritative *Oxford English Dictionary* didn't include the word ecosocialism until 2008. The first citation it provides for the word is in *The Times* in 1985. In fact, the word was at least five years old then.

14. For key articles from this period, many of which were first published in CNS, see Martin O'Connor, ed, *Is Capitalism Sustainable?: Political Economy and the Politics of Ecology* (Guilford, 1994), and Ted Benton, ed, *The Greening of Marxism* (Guilford, 1996). James O'Connor set out his views at length in *Natural Causes: Essays in Ecological Marxism* (Guilford, 1998).

limited its influence outside of academia.

So far as I can find, the first book to argue for "bringing Marxist analysis much more into ecologism's mainstream," was *Eco-Socialism: From Deep Ecology to Social Justice* (1993) by British environmentalist David Pepper. In his view Marxism doesn't offer "a complete eco-socialist theory," but "can at the very least constantly provide an antidote to the vagueness, incoherence, woolly-mindedness and occasional vapidity that can invade mainstream and anarchist green discourse".[15]

The problem with that approach, as with much ecosocialist debate in the 1990s, was that it sought to merge two approaches that did not mix well — overlaying Marxism on green theory, or vice versa. Important as those discussions were, the hybrids they produced weren't viable. To escape that cul-de-sac, ecosocialism had to find new beginnings.

Marxist ecosocialism

As it became obvious that "Marxism plus ecologism" was a dead end, some socialist activists and scholars adopted a different approach, by returning to basics and studying what Marx and Engels actually wrote about the relationship between human society and nature. They found, contrary to common criticisms, that Marx had developed an ecological critique of capitalism, a critique that offers a philosophical, economic and scientific basis for modern ecosocialism. The work of John Bellamy Foster and Paul Burkett was particularly important in the process of rediscovering that critique. They showed, in Burkett's words, that Marxism is not an alternative to environmentalism, but rather "a particular kind of environmentalism, one that considers people-nature relations from the standpoint of class relations and the requirements of human liberation".[16]

In *Marx's Ecology: Materialism and Nature* (2000), John Bellamy Foster undertook a systematic reconstruction of

---

15. David Pepper, *Eco-Socialism: From Deep Ecology to Social Justice* (Routledge, 1993), p248.

16. Paul Burkett, *Marx and Nature: A Red and Green Perspective,* 2nd ed (Haymarket, 2014)

Marx's ecological thought. He showed that Marx's materialist understanding of history and nature, combined with his careful study of soil chemistry and agriculture, brought him to conclusions that were ahead of the science of his day. Indeed, they were ahead of much of what passes for ecological thought today. "Marx's work cannot be fully comprehended without an understanding of his materialist conception of nature, and its relation to the materialist conception of history. Marx's social thought, in other words, is inextricably bound to an ecological world-view".[17]

A central achievement of Foster's research was his rediscovery of the importance of metabolism and metabolic rift for Marx's analysis of capitalism.

> An essential component of the concept of metabolism has always been the notion that it constitutes the basis on which the complex web of interactions necessary to life is sustained, and growth becomes possible. Marx employed the concept of a 'rift' in the metabolic relation between human beings and the earth to capture the material estrangement of human beings within capitalist society from the natural conditions which formed the basis for their existence — what he called 'the everlasting nature-imposed condition[s] of human existence'.[18]

Burkett also systematically studied Marx's works, primarily from the standpoint of political economy. In *Marx and Nature: A Red and Green Perspective* (1999), he showed that common green criticisms of Marxism — for example, that Marx favored industrial growth at all costs, or that he thought nature had no limits and no value — reflect fundamental misunderstandings. Marx's work in political economy "provides original and useful insights

17. John Bellamy Foster, *Marx's Ecology: Materialism and Nature* (Monthly Review, 2000), p20
18. Foster, *Marx's Ecology*, as above, p153.

into the sources of environmental crisis under capitalism, the relations between ecological struggles and class struggles, and the requirements of a healthy and sustainable co-evolution of humanity and nature".[19]

After disproving the common green argument that "that Marx's diagnosis of the contradictions and crises of capitalism had nothing to do with the natural conditions of production," Burkett showed that Marx identified two different kinds of specifically environmental crises. There are crises caused by shortages of natural materials (cotton in the 1860s, oil in the 1970s, for example), and there are crises caused by the degradation of the conditions necessary for life.

> [It is] essential to distinguish environmental crises of capital accumulation from environmental crisis in the sense of a general deterioration of the conditions for the development of people as a natural and social species. The latter type of crisis by no means automatically implies the former, even though both are products of capitalism — which is to say that from the standpoint of human development, capitalism is an ecologically and socially irrational system.[20]

In the second edition of *Marx and Nature*, Burkett re-emphasised the importance of the second type of environmental crisis, relating it specifically to Marx's concept of metabolic rift, as rediscovered and extended by John Bellamy Foster.

> In light of more recent work by Foster and others, it is now possible to affirm that Marx's metabolic rift approach — when properly reconstructed and updated to account for developments in technology, natural science, and the further globalization of capital

19. Burkett, *Marx and Nature*, as above, p6.
20. Burkett, *Marx and Nature*, as above, p196.

accumulation — can help us understand the systemic roots of the contemporary problems of climate change, depletion and degradation of oceanic ecosystems by industrial fishing and aquaculture, and disruptions to the global nitrogen cycle brought on by overuse of inorganic fertilizers in industrial agriculture. The rift approach has also been proven useful for demonstrating how ecological imperialism (the guano trade, sugar plantations, etc) and resultant ecological crises have been central to the entire history of capitalist development and underdevelopment on a global scale.[21]

Inferior crises?

There's a common leftist view — a prejudice, really — that economics is more important than all the rest of Marxist theory, that economic struggles are more important than other social conflicts, and that only economic crises are real crises of capitalism. That view underlies various efforts to correct or update Marx by showing that ecological damage leads inevitably to economic crises.

James O'Connor, for example, wrote that although Marx thought capitalist farming degraded the soil, he failed to "put two and two together," and "never considered the possibility" that ecological destruction "might raise the costs of the elements of capital, which, in turn, might threaten an economic crisis." This blind spot prevented Marx from developing an "'ecological' theory of crisis and social transformation".[22] O'Connor's proposed "second contradiction of capitalism" was an attempt to correct Marx's failure by focusing on damage to capitalism's "conditions of production".

Similarly, sociologist Alan Rudy, in a sharply critical commentary on Marx's Ecology, argued that "Marx underdeveloped his analysis of the role of ecological crisis in crises of

21. Burkett, *Marx and Nature,* as above, ppxix-xx.
22. O'Connor, *Natural Causes,* as above, p160.

capitalism." In Rudy's view, Foster "overstates the importance of ecological conditions and contradictions in Marx's work," because "Marx did not theorize the 'metabolic rift' as an important moment in the crisis tendencies of capitalism".[23]

More recently, Jason W Moore, whose approach is similar to O'Connor's, has criticised supporters of metabolic rift theory and others for failing to show "how the circuit of capital links up with actually existing technological and environmental change," and for basing their analysis on "a powerfully Cartesian divide between accounts of (so-called) 'economic' crisis and (so-called) 'environmental' crisis".[24] Moore proposes a "singular theory" that attributes accumulation crises to the periodic depletion of "cheap nature," and a "tendency for the ecological surplus to fall".[25]

Such arguments presume that economic crises are more serious, or more potentially revolutionary, than ecological crises. But as Foster argues, it is precisely because there is no feedback mechanism between environmental degradation and capitalist profitability that environmental crises are so very dangerous.

> We should not underestimate capitalism's capacity to accumulate in the midst of the most blatant ecological destruction, to profit from environmental degradation (for example through the growth of the waste management industry), and to continue to destroy the earth to the point of no return — both for human society and for most of the world's living species. In other words, the dangers of a deepening ecological problem are all

23. Alan Rudy, "Rejoinders," *Capitalism Nature Socialism*, vol 12, no 3, (2001), p143; and "Marx's Ecology and Rift Analysis," *Capitalism Nature Socialism*, vol 12, no 2 (2001), p61.

24. Jason W Moore, "Transcending the metabolic rift: a theory of crises in the capitalist world-ecology", *Journal of Peasant Studies*, vol 38, no 1 (2011), p10, p39.

25. Moore, who invented the concept of "ecological surplus," admits it is "an imperfect formulation" that "cannot be quantified." It is difficult to understand how an unquantified measure could be said to fall, or how it could have a measurable effect on profits. His full argument is in *Capitalism in the Web of Life* (Verso, 2015), especially chapter 4.

the more serious because the system does not have an internal (or external) regulatory mechanism that causes it to reorganize. There is no ecological counterpart to the business cycle...

Focusing on conditions of production and the 'second contradiction' of capitalism tends to downplay the full dimensions of the ecological crisis and even of capitalism's impact on the environment in the process of trying to force everything into the locked box of a specific economic crisis theory.[26]

Method, not scripture

Marx's Ecology and *Marx and Nature* were major works of de-revision that systematically examined what Marx and Engels actually wrote about nature and ecology, and cleared away myths and distortions that had inhibited the development of ecological Marxism.

One thing that they did not do, contrary to some critics, is treat Marx and Engels as infallible or "consider the original Marxian canon as the true and sufficient guide to save nature from capitalism".[27] As Foster replied, that suggestion is "an absolute absurdity".

No rational individual could believe that Marx's nineteenth-century analysis, notwithstanding all its brilliance, constitutes a 'sufficient guide' to solving the global ecological crisis an age of planetary climate change, ocean acidification, and fracking. Naturally, whatever methodological insights are to be derived from Marx's dialectic with respect to the ecological and social critique of capitalism...have to be synthesized with a

26. John Bellamy Foster, *The Ecological Revolution: Making Peace with the Planet* (Monthly Review, 2009), pp206-7.

27. Joel Kovel, *The Enemy of Nature: the End of Capitalism or the End of the World?* (Zed Books, 2002), 211.

vast body of historical and scientific knowledge that has arisen subsequently, and with the conditions of contemporary social praxis.[28]

As Kohei Saito shows in his pathbreaking book *Karl Marx's Ecosocialism,* Marx himself didn't believe in and certainly didn't offer eternal truths about the human-nature relationship.

He aimed instead at comprehending material limits under respective concrete conditions of natural sciences and technology. Where exactly this contradiction manifests itself is not given a priori; it requires a concrete analysis of each situation. Natural sciences provide the basic knowledge for such an analysis. Otherwise, a critique would only be able to say that capitalism must destroy the environment. Marx was never satisfied with such an abstract thesis.[29]

What Burkett and Foster and others who have followed their lead find in Marx is not inerrant scripture, but rather, as Saito says, "a solid methodological foundation for the analysis of capital's historical process of antagonism between humanity and nature". [30]

Of course, recovering Marx's ecological method is only a beginning. In his landmark book on capitalism's impact on medicine and human health, *The Second Sickness*, Howard Waitzkin notes that 20th Century Marxism often suffered from "a dogmatic application of the theories of its founders," and failure "to grapple with current realities that the classics of Marxism did not anticipate." Theory is not enough: a materialist approach requires historical specificity. "Marxist analysis tries to explain social problems with historical concreteness

28. John Bellamy Foster, "Foreword" to Burkett, *Marx and Nature*, 2nd ed, as above, ppx-xi.

29. Kohei Saito, *Karl Marx's Ecosocialism: Capitalism, Nature, and the Unfinished Critique of Political Economy* (Monthly Review, 2017), p260.

30. Saito, *Karl Marx's Ecosocialism*, as above, p260.

and with reference to specific material reality. Although general analytic principles may be appropriate to the study of different problems, each problem has its own context which demands concrete explanation".[31]

In that respect, it is significant that, as historian and environmentalist Andreas Malm writes, "one Marxist line of inquiry into environmental problems has outshone all others in creativity and productivity: the theory of the metabolic rift".[32] Over the past two decades, there has been a remarkable outpouring of articles and books that use the concept of "an irreparable rift in the interdependent process of social metabolism" to concretely analyse a wide range of environmental issues, including climate change, conservation, antibiotic resistance, biodiversity, sewage disposal, agriculture, fishery collapse, soil erosion, and more.[33]

Moving forward, these ideas and analyses will be tested in action, by the contribution they make to moving beyond interpreting the world, to changing it. Only a society that is committed to working with the natural world instead of against it can heal the deep metabolic rifts that capitalism has created, and only a mass ecosocialist movement can make such a society possible. Creating an ecological society will not be fast or easy, but it is the most important challenge facing humanity in our time.

***

31. Howard Waitzkin, *The Second Sickness: Contradictions of Capitalist Health Care*, Revised edition (Rowman & Littlefield, 2000), p7.

32. Andreas Malm, *The Progress of this Storm: Nature and Society in a Warming World* (Verso, 2018), p177.

33. "The Metabolic Rift: A Selected Bibliography," published online by Monthly Review and periodically updated by Ryan Wishart, R Jamil Jonna, and Jordan Besek, is an invaluable resource. *https://monthlyreview.org/commentary/metabolic-rift/*

Chapter 4
Karl Marx's Idea of Ecosocialism in the 21st Century
Kohei Saito

For many years, environmentalists and even many self-proclaimed Marxists believed that Marx held a Promethean viewpoint, i.e. hyper-industrialist support for the domination of society over nature, and fell into an uncritical endorsement of technological development under capitalism. One obvious reason for this rejection of Marx's ecology is that Marx did not finish *Capital*. Marx eagerly studied natural sciences in his late years with a clear ecological perspective, but he was not able to fully integrate his new findings into *Capital*. Marx only left a number of notebooks on natural sciences. Unfortunately, no one paid attention to these notebooks after his death and they were almost completely forgotten in the archive.

Why was this work neglected? "Traditional Marxism" treated Marx's materialist project as a closed dialectical system that explains everything in the universe, including human history and nature. In this sense, Marxists did not pay enough attention to his economic manuscripts and even less to notebooks, which document the incomplete character of Marx's *Capital*.

Of course, there were Marxists who rejected this omnipotent

reading by traditional Marxism. They are known today under the banner of "Western Marxism". However, when they rejected traditional Marxism, they harshly reproached Engels as the misleading founder of traditional Marxism, who wrongly expanded Marx's dialectical critique of capitalist society to the scientific system of the universe. Consequently, when Western Marxists expelled Engels and his dialectics of nature, they also excluded the sphere of nature and natural sciences from their analysis. Consequently, Marx's serious engagement with the natural sciences was ignored by both traditional and Western Marxists.

But today, with the publication of Marx's notebooks in the *Marx-Engels-Gesamtausgabe*, it is possible to rescue Marx's ecological critique of capitalism, as already begun by ecosocialists such as Paul Burkett and John Bellamy Foster.[1] It is also quite apparent today that mass production and consumption under capitalism has tremendous influence upon the global landscape and causes ecological crisis. Marxist theory thus needs to respond to the situation with a clear practical demand to envision a sustainable society beyond capitalism. Capitalism and material conditions for sustainable production are incompatible. This is the basic insight of "ecosocialism."

Marx clearly recognised the destructive power of capital and argued that disruptions in the universal metabolism of nature inevitably undermine material conditions for free and sustainable human development. The robbery inherent in the capitalist development of productive forces does not bring about progress which leads to the future society. Rather, Marx attempted to analyse how the logic of capital diverges from the eternal natural cycle and ultimately causes various disharmonies in the metabolic interaction between humans and nature. He analysed this point with reference to Justus von Liebig's critique of modern "robbery agriculture," which takes as much nutrition as possible from the soil without returning it. Robbery agriculture is driven

1. Paul Burkett, *Marx and Nature* (Palgrave, 1999); John Bellamy Foster, *Marx's Ecology* (Monthly Review Press, 2000).

by the need to maximise profits in the short term, which means that the material conditions of the soil become simply incompatible with sustainable production. Thus, there emerges a grave gap between the logic of capital's valorisation and that of nature's metabolism, which creates "metabolic rifts" in human interaction with the environment.

Though Marx in *Capital* mainly discusses this problem of metabolic rift in relation to soil exhaustion, it is not at all necessary to limit it to this. Marx himself also tried to apply this theoretical concept to various issues in his later life such as deforestation and stock farming. So Marx would be happy to see that today there are various attempts to apply this theoretical framework as a tool to analyse ongoing environmental crisis. To name a few, Stefano B. Longo's analysis of marine ecology, Ryan Gunderson's critique of livestock agribusiness, as well as Philip Mancus's discussion on the disruption of nitrogen cycle are excellent examples for the contemporary ecosocialist application of Marx's theory of metabolic rift.[2]

Marx believed that as long as the capitalist system persists, there exists an inevitable tendency toward the degradation of the material conditions of production. In other words, the market cannot function as a good mediator for sustainable production in contrast to the persistent liberal belief that green capitalism is somehow possible in the near future. Capitalist innovation will not solve the ecological crisis either, as history clearly demonstrates.

Since there is very little time left for us, the liberal hope that carbon trading or other market mechanisms can solve climate change or other environmental crises only functions as an ideological tool to distract us from confronting the real danger and threat. In this sense Liberals are very dangerous — offering the free market as a solution as if it could automatically solve the

2. See for instance: Stefano B Longo et al, *The Tragedy of the Commodity* (Rutgers University Press, 2015); Ryan Gunderson, "The Metabolic Rifts of Livestock Agribusiness", *Organisation and Environment*, vol. 24, issue 4, December 2011, pp404-422; Philip Mancus, "Nitrogen Fertilizer Dependency and Its Contradictions: A Theoretical Exploration of Social-Ecological Metabolism", *Rural Sociology*, vol. 72, issue 2, October 2009, pp269-288.

problem without a conscious attempt to radically change the existing mode of production.

Ultimately, it does not matter for capital accumulation if a large part of the planet becomes unsuitable for life. Marx realised that technological development is organised as "productive forces of capital," which lead to the full realisation of negative aspects of technologies, so they cannot function as a material foundation for socialist society. This problem is discernible from the fact that capital can profit even from environmental disaster. As Naomi Klein has documented in detail, this is clearly visible in what neoliberal "disaster capitalism" has done in the last decades.[3] Consequently, capital can actually continue to make profit from the current ecological crises by inventing new business opportunities such as geo-engineering, GMOs, carbon trading, and natural disaster insurance. Thus, natural limits do not lead to the collapse of the capitalist system. Capitalism can keep going beyond these limits, but the current level of civilisation cannot exist beyond a certain limit. This is why a serious engagement with global warming simultaneously requires a conscious struggle against capitalism on a global scale.

Using the example of the exhaustion of Irish soil due to British colonialism, Marx showed how the expansion of capital around the world is directly linked to ecological crisis in colonial countries. In the key passage on the concept of the metabolic rift, Marx wrote, in the third volume of *Capital*, that the capitalist mode of production "produces conditions that provoke an irreparable rift in the interdependent process between social metabolism and natural metabolism prescribed by the natural laws of the soil. The result of this is a squandering of the vitality of the soil, and *trade carries this devastation far beyond the bounds of a single country* (Liebig)." With an expansion of capitalist accumulation, the metabolic rift becomes a global issue.

Marx has been proven right, as this is exactly what we are witnessing today, especially with climate change. Climate

3. Naomi Klein, *The Shock Doctrine* (Penguin, 2007).

change will not put an end to the regime of capital — it is likely to continue to accumulate capital, even if the ecological crisis deepens to destroy the entire planet and to globally produce a mass of environmental refugees and a so-called "environmental proletariat" whose condition of existence — not simply their working conditions — is severely degraded due to capitalist accumulation. Rich people will survive, while the poor become much more vulnerable to environmental disaster, even though they are much less responsible for the crisis. The fight for climate justice clearly includes a component of class struggle, and the environmental proletariat can emerge as a revolutionary subject to protect their health, community and the environment against the worsening economic and ecological crisis.

While climate change could change everything about our life, changing climate change will mean changing capitalism. This is how ecosocialism comprehends ecological crisis and metabolic rifts as the central contradiction of capitalism. Marx was one of the first ecosocialists, as he recognised when he found a "socialist tendency" in Carl Fraas's warning against excessive deforestation and climate change. Thus, to overcome alienation from nature is a central task for both Red and Green, which can be realised only beyond capitalism, and not within "green capitalism". Marx's critique of the metabolic rift provides a methodological foundation for a critical analysis of the current global ecological crisis; it is our task today to substantiate and update Marx's ecology for the 21st century by developing the synthetic analysis of political economy and natural sciences as a radical critique of capitalism.

***

Chapter 5
Natural Capital: A Neoliberal Response

Ian Rappel

Capitalism has placed humanity on a devastating collision course with living nature.[1] In its 40-year neoliberal phase alone it has unleashed a scale of ecological destruction that has few precedents across Earth's entire geological history — we are teetering on the brink of a sixth mass extinction event. While we are not short of examples of the horrors unleashed by capitalism, this wanton destruction of non-human life in its myriad and amazing forms is surely one of the most obvious markers of our descent towards barbarism.[2]

The unrelenting ecological degradation of the neoliberal era is all the more alarming when we reflect that organs of environmental resistance have been flourishing during this period. Environmental NGOs and pressure groups now number in their hundreds across the world and membership numbers are

1. This article originally appeared in *International Socialism* 160, autumn 2018. I am grateful for comments and feedback on my original article from Bram Büscher, Alex Callinicos, Martin Empson, Camilla Royle, Sian Sullivan and Colin Tudge.

2. Ian Rappel, "Capitalism and Species Extinction", *International Socialism* 147, summer 2015. *http://isj.org.uk/capitalism-and-species-extinction/*

higher than those of most mainstream political parties.[3] While the situation for biodiversity would be worse in the absence of these groups, their work and occasional victories have failed to stem the tide of extinction and ecological devastation derived from capitalism's accumulation process.

For environmental conservationists the frustrations and growing awareness of the scale of the challenge have lately led to some surprising tactical and philosophical directions.[4] In particular, the drive to assign monetary value to biodiversity and nature is being portrayed as a necessary means of translating the environmental message to legislators, business and the markets. This argument for nature financialisation — the processes by which banks and financiers have turned to environmental conservation as a new front for speculative investment, and the simultaneous rewriting of conservation to fit banking and financial concepts — has gained momentum and acceptance across environmental science and politics during the last decade as economic recession/depression and austerity have dominated global economic architectures.

The concept of "natural capital" (NC) that has developed through this drift towards financialisation has now taken firm and favourable root within mainstream environmental politics. Essentially, in the spirit of the old Quaker maxim "speak truth unto power", some environmentalists are presenting the need to assign monetary value to biodiversity, ecology and nature as a form of political pragmatism. Critiques of NC within conservation, meanwhile, are being suppressed through false consensus

3. The World Wide Fund for Nature (WWF) — the self-proclaimed "world's leading conservation organisation" — has more than 1 million members in the United States and 5 million globally. The Royal Society for the Protection of Birds (RSPB) in the UK has over 1 million members. Greenpeace claims 130,000 supporters in the UK and 2.8 million around the world. In early 2018 the Labour Party had 552,000 members, the Conservatives 124,000, Scottish National Party (SNP) had 118,000, Liberal Democrats 101,000, Green Party 41,000, UK Independence Party (UKIP) 21,000 and Plaid Cymru 8,000 members.

4. See the discussion of this in Ieuan Churchill, "Environmentalism in Crisis: Neoliberal Conservation and Wilderness Romanticism", *International Socialism* 142, spring 2014. http://isj.org.uk/environmentalism-in-crisis-neoliberal-conservation-and-wilderness-romanticism/

and the well-rehearsed Thatcherite TINA — "there is no alternative" — mantra.

Modern campaigning environmentalism can trace it roots back to the social and political movements that erupted 50 years ago. Organisations such as Greenpeace and Friends of the Earth rose directly from the anti-Vietnam War movements to challenge the ecological destruction that was being revealed across the world during the 1960s and early 1970s.[5] Alongside direct action and the development of ecological science, many environmentalists embarked on a quest for alternative and counter-cultural or anti-capitalist values. Native American history and culture provided a particularly rich seam of influence for environmental romantics and the ecological elements of individualist lifestyle politics. A poorly-translated and Hollywood-manipulated "speech" by Chief Si'ahl (Seattle) was particularly popular, and one suite of questions in the speech was for many decades held aloft as a central ethic within environmentalism: "How can you buy or sell the sky, the warmth of the land?... If we do not own the freshness of the air and the sparkle of the water, how can you buy them?" Today, almost a half-century later, it is astounding to think that the answers to these profound (if sadly apocryphal) questions have come from within environmentalism itself. For today's neoliberal or pragmatic environmentalists, the answer is natural capital.

Natural capital

Natural capital can be interpreted as a concept in which, "nature and the 'natural world' [are] approached in terms of asset values for human organisations and societies that can be calculated in monetary units using economic and accounting techniques".[6] It represents an increasingly popular attempt on

5. Robert Hunter, *The Greenpeace To Amchitka: An Environmental Odyssey* (Arsenal Pulp Press, 2014).

6. Sian Sullivan, "Noting some Effects of Fabricating 'Nature' as 'Natural Capital'", *The Ecological Citizen*, volume 1, number 1, 2017, p66. *www.ecologicalcitizen.net/article. php?t=noting-some-effects-fabricating-nature-natural-capital*

the part of certain environmental economists to identify and apply mainly quantitative, financial values to the components of ecology that underpin human society. The species, habitats and ecosystems that constitute society's natural capital provide various and wide-ranging "ecosystem services" — ranging from indirect or generalised services such as water quality, to direct and specific services such as fishery yields. The condition of these units as defined in qualitative and quantitative terms, represent the "stock" of natural capital (figure 1). Monitoring of the stock's condition can be achieved through the development of natural capital accounting tools, and the outputs of these are increasingly used to determine the state and trajectory of biodiversity under prevailing economic and policy conditions.

Figure 1: The natural capital framework

Stocks: Natural capital (living and non living resources)	Flows: Ecosystems and abiotic services (e.g. flood protection, recreation)	Value: Benefits to business and society

Source: *Natural Capital Coalition, 2016.*[7]

The approach has been developed by environmental economists who are concerned by the general failures of capitalism's price allocations for biodiversity, ecology and ecosystems. In the current system, environmental degradation appears as a so-called market "externality" — in other words, it doesn't represent a direct financial cost to the polluter. Instead, NC identifies the value of these hitherto economically-hidden elements of society, helping states and businesses to quantify their ecological impact and steer their policies accordingly. An effective NC approach relies on acceptance of a framework in which

7. Natural Capital Coalition, "What is Natural Capital?", 2016. *https://naturalcapitalcoalition. org/natural-capital/*

monetary value is assigned to nature to a maximum feasible degree (full financial valuation is tempered with a slight nod to "ethical" considerations).[8]

The historical response to biodiversity loss

Before outlining the problems with NC it is worth considering how the concept fits within the historical landscape and politics of environmental conservation. Prior to the 1960s, species conservation was influenced mainly by a philosophy of wilderness romanticism. The poetic narrative embedded in influential work by the likes of Aldo Leopold and John Muir in the US, and Gilbert White and Lord Rothschild in the UK, led to a land ethic dominated by the need to "protect" landscapes from human interference through partition into nature reserves and national parks.[9]

Thus, for the first half of the 20th century, ambitious attempts were made to carve out and preserve parcels of land for nature and wildlife. The most influential initiatives came from the US, where large areas such as Yosemite National Park were established for landscapes that appeared devoid of human interference but which had actually been wiped clean of indigenous influence by disease, war and racist land-grabs. Throughout Africa, European colonial powers created similar "game reserves" (with similar devastating cultural impact) to enhance wildlife populations for hunting and the "safari" culture. These reserves are today the source of amazing media images of "wild Africa" that feed Western appetites for wildlife conservation. But their artificial and often violent history is hidden from view.[10]

8. RSPB, "Accounting for Nature: A Natural Capital Account of the RSPB's Estate in England", 2017, p10. *www.rspb.org.uk/globalassets/downloads/documents/positions/economics/accounting-for-nature.pdf*

9. Rory Spowers, *Rising Tides: The History and Future of the Environmental Movement* (Canongate, 2002).

10. William Adams, *Against Extinction: The Story of Conservation* (Earthscan, 2004); Jonathan Adams and Thomas McShane, *The Myth of Wild Africa: Conservation Without Illusion* (Norton, 1992); Mark Dowie, *Conservation Refugees: The Hundred-Year Conflict Between Global Conservation and Native Peoples* (The MIT Press, 2009).

Across the USSR, the pre-revolutionary interest in nature reserve development was encouraged by Lenin and the Bolsheviks to protect vast swathes of land as zapovedniki — nature reserves that could serve the joint objectives of wilderness protection and scientific research.[11] This latter approach entailed maintaining "natural" areas as comparative laboratories against land that was earmarked for agricultural and industrial improvement — a more rational methodology that saved much of the former USSR's biodiversity from post-war industrialisation but which is now threatened by market capitalism across Russia today.

Environmental conservation, for much of the 20th century, was dominated by this land preservation ethos. And many of the world's "natural" parks and monuments have developed into hotspots for biodiversity despite, or because of, their artificial origins. However, by the 1960s it was becoming obvious, thanks to the work of Rachel Carson and others,[12] that ecological degradation outside of these protected areas was accelerating through post-war industrialisation, particularly in agriculture. Radicalism infected parts of the ecology movement during the 1960s and early 1970s — inspired by images of Agent Orange defoliant use by the US during the Vietnam War and harrowing scenes of industrial whaling. Whether fuelled by these events or the countervailing tendency of neo-Malthusianism and "Population Bomb" rhetoric, the 1970s and 1980s witnessed a remarkable growth in environmental awareness and produced a consensus of concern over biodiversity loss and associated degradation.[13]

By the 1990s, at the close of the Cold War, there was much optimism within mainstream environmentalism that humanity would finally cooperate and coordinate its efforts to address

11. Douglas R Weiner, *Models of Nature: Ecology, Conservation and Cultural Revolution in Soviet Russia* (University of Pittsburgh Press, 1988).

12. Rachel Carson, *Silent Spring* (Penguin, 2000 [1962]).

13. Paul Ehrlich, *The Population Bomb: Population Control or Race to Oblivion* (Ballantine Books, 1968); Jeremy Cherfas, *The Hunting of the Whale: A Tragedy That Must End* (Penguin, 1989).

global environmental problems. Consequently, many of the outcomes of the 1992 Rio "Earth" Summit, such as the concept of "sustainable development" and the Convention on Biological Diversity (CBD), were framed in a positive light despite critical voices that warned that the agenda at Rio '92 was being shaped by Western hegemony and that vital issues of corporate power were being sidelined.[14] Indeed, by the time of the Rio+10 Summit in Johannesburg, the atmosphere had turned sour. Ten years of neoliberal reforms across the Third World had seen living conditions stagnate or decline in what became known as the "Lost Decade" for development. On the ecological front, the empowerment of multinational corporations and of a growing Third World capitalist class gave rise to increased biodiversity loss as rainforests and other ecosystems were replaced by cash crops and landless peasants were forced onto the ecological margins or into urban slums.[15] The 1990s witnessed a concentration of global power in the hands of Western governments, particularly the US, extending their influence over the Bretton Woods Institutions (International Monetary Fund, World Bank and World Trade Organisation) and undermining any alternatives to neoliberal economic reforms (by implementing Structural Adjustment Programmes) as part of the so-called Washington Consensus.

After a decade of frustration with neoliberal globalisation, many environmental activist groups and conservation NGOs began voicing their concerns over the ecological impact of the growing material and power discrepancies between the wealthy minority and the poorest sections of global society. Between 1999 and 2001 environmental activists and NGOs played an important role in the global anti-capitalist movement that emerged to challenge the neoliberal agenda of "globalisation" at several high-powered international meetings (Seattle WTO

14. Neil Middleton, Phil O'Keefe and Sam Moyo, *Tears of the Crocodile: From Rio to Reality in the Third World* (Pluto Press, 1993); David Treece, "Why the Earth Summit Failed", *International Socialism* 56, autumn 1992. *http://isj.org.uk/why-the-earth-summit-failed/*

15. Ian Rappel and Neil Thomas, "An Examination of the Compatibility of World Bank Policies towards Population, Development and Biodiversity in the Third World", *The Environmentalist*, volume 18, issue 2, 1998.

in 1999, Genoa G8 in 2001). Even large mainstream conservation NGOs such as WWF were caught up in the anti-capitalist mood at the turn of the century — publishing radical critiques of biodiversity loss that looked explicitly at the interactions between poverty and ecology. [16]

But the first decade of the 21st century was not dominated by anti-capitalism or its environmental possibilities. Instead, 9/11, Western wars in Afghanistan and Iraq, and the so-called War on Terror defined all major agendas. Simultaneously, environmentalism was rocked back on its heels by strong post-Seattle criticisms of NGOs within Western politics and across the business press.[17] Indeed, the US proved so bullish in its foreign policy during this decade that it barely even acknowledged the 2002 Rio+10 Summit in Johannesburg, arguing that potentially excessive criticism of corporations by environmental NGOs made the summit irrelevant.

Between 2002 and 2012 (when the United Nations Conference on Sustainable Development returned to Brazil for "Rio+20") the political direction of mainstream environmental conservation was thrown into sharp reverse. At Rio+20 concepts such as natural capital were controversially promoted as "Green Economy" initiatives despite opposition from many activists and Third World delegates.[18] Environmental NGOs — disciplined by state violence at Seattle and Genoa and increasingly entangled with neoliberal government agendas through the development of professional lobbying — appear to have been finally caught up in the trawl net of neoliberal ideology.

Since the 1970s, in a world where field experience pointed to an unfolding biodiversity crisis, conservationists (knowingly or otherwise) had been wrestling with strategies to preserve species

16. Alexander Wood, Pamela Stedman-Edwards and Johanna Mang (eds), *The Root Causes of Biodiversity Loss* (WWF/Earthscan, 2000). WWF sent a delegation to the demonstrations at the Genoa G8 summit.

17. "The Case for Globalisation", *Economist*, 23 September 2000, *www.economist.com/printedition/2000-09-23-0*

18. Martin Empson, "Fiddling While Rome Burns: A Report from Rio", *Irish Marxist Review*, volume 1, number 3, 2012 *www.irishmarxistreview.net/index.php/imr/issue/view/3*

and ecosystems in the face of a growing capitalist onslaught of commodification and profiteering. A desperate sense of urgency, combined with the political difficulties of confronting capitalism, had left many activists and NGOs in a state of paralysis by the time of the 2008 global economic downturn. The sudden implementation of global austerity, combined with calls to loosen environmental regulations, drove a gradual breakdown of the Rio '92 consensus over sustainable development and the CBD. In attempting to maintain political relevance and access to private sector funding many conservationists became increasingly attracted to a new environmental lexicon that was being developed by the United Nations and other international bodies such as the World Bank. Within the influential Millennium Ecosystems Assessment (MEA) report,[19] and the work of The Economics of Ecosystems and Biodiversity (TEEB) project,[20] novel environmental metaphors were developed.[21] Ecology and biodiversity, and the functions that flowed from them, were increasingly described as "ecosystem services" and markets in these being worked up as Payments for Ecosystem Services (PES). Uncritical and enthusiastic adoption of this language opened the door to an overarching neoliberal "solution" to species loss, with its emphasis on financialisation and the market — natural capital.[22]

The economic ancestry of natural capital

One of the world's leading advocates for natural capital is Professor Dieter Helm, Fellow in Economics at New College

19. See *www.millenniumassessment.org/en/index.html*

20. TEEB, *The Economics of Ecosystems and Biodiversity: Ecological and Economic Foundations* (Earthscan, 2010); Karachepone Ninan, *Conservation and Valuing Ecosystem Services and Biodiversity: Economic, Institutional and Social Challenges* (Earthscan, 2009).

21. Many of these concepts have their roots in the early discussions on "green capitalism" that were circulating on the fringes of mainstream environmentalism during the late 1980s.

22. An excellent critical overview and assessment of neoliberal conservation can be found in Bram Büscher, Wolfram Dressler and Robert Fletcher (eds), *Nature™ Inc: Environmental Conservation in the Neoliberal Age* (University of Arizona Press, 2014). Sian Sullivan's pamphlet for the Third World Network also gives a useful introduction to the evolution of natural capital and nature financialisation. See Sian Sullivan, *Financialisation, Biodiversity Conservation and Equity: Some Currents and Concerns* (Third World Network, 2012).

Oxford and Chair of the UK's Natural Capital Committee. Helm's arguments for natural capital follow quite standard lines of neoclassical supply and demand economics:

> For much of the conventional economy, prices and costs are accepted as the way to allocate resources. Markets are the social institutions through which demand and supply are brought together, and equilibrium is found where prices and quantities match people's willingness to pay with companies' willingness to produce. Changes in demand and supply work themselves out through markets... Markets are all about the allocation of scarce resources... Humans impact on almost all of nature now and, where there is no price, and hence no cost to the users of these natural resources, there is no incentive to conserve them.[23]

In this context environmental destruction is framed as a product of economic inefficiency. Many converts to NC — responding to the staggering scale of the biodiversity crisis, and a cynicism or disbelief in the potential for social movements to win change — agree with Helm on this.[24] According to the RSPB:

> Our economic system continues to fail to reflect the importance of nature in decisions that affect it. This long-term failure is at the heart of the over-exploitation of and under-investment in nature that has driven so much of the destruction of the natural world — a loss for both people and nature.

A Natural Capital approach sets out a framework that

23. Dieter Helm, *Natural Capital: Valuing the Earth* (Yale University Press, 2016), p117.

24. I am grateful for Martin Empson's input on this point. Tony Juniper, formerly Executive Director for Friends of the Earth UK, is one of the highest profile advocates of NC, and has declared his new role at WWF to be one of Natural Capital advocacy — Tony Juniper, *What Has Nature Ever Done For Us? How Money Really Does Grow on Trees* (Profile Books, 2013); Tony Juniper, *What Nature Does for Britain* (Profile Books, 2015).

can address this failure, by better reflecting the values of nature during decision-making. If widely adopted, it could deliver huge benefits for nature and people.[25]

The most extreme supporters of NC blend this neoclassical analysis with a neoliberal argument that environmental regulations are both ineffective and undesirable acts of market distortion. They advocate the establishment of mechanisms to enhance Payments for Ecosystem Services (PES) and biodiversity offsetting. It is no small coincidence that these arguments are being made at this time — with land and resources facing privatisation through austerity.

Moderate advocates of natural capital are careful to qualify their enthusiasm for financialisation with a demand that biodiversity is also valued for its "intrinsic" worth. While arguing for a need to consider moral and ethical elements of nature conservation, they propose methods such as natural capital accounting as a monitoring tool that can objectively audit the impact of society — positive or negative — on biodiversity and nature. Given the recently revealed history of accounting trickery and outright fraud associated with finance under neoliberalism, this search for "objectivity" seems naïve if not counterproductive.

(Un)natural capital

Raymond Williams, in his discussion of human-nature relationships, argued that "It will be ironic if one of the last forms of the separation between abstracted Man and abstracted Nature is an intellectual separation between economics and ecology. It will be a sign that we are beginning to think in some necessary ways when we can conceive these becoming, as they ought to become, a single discipline".[26] Many of its advocates conclude that NC represents a significant step towards this disciplinary unity — one whereby nature can be integrated with economics

25. RSPB, "Accounting for Nature", as above.
26. Raymond Williams, *Culture and Materialism* (Verso, 2005), p84.

through a calculation of its monetary value so that the full costs of exploitation are revealed, and market failure and externalities are ameliorated. Indeed, it is important to note that a strong environmental ethic lies firmly at the heart of NC. In many ways the development of the concept is implicit acknowledgement of the fact that humanity and nature are closely interrelated but that capitalism does not recognise the roles and functions of living nature within its social metabolism (thus widening the "metabolic rift" highlighted so well by John Bellamy Foster and others). In locating the source of the environmental crisis with the failure of the capitalist system, NC is an improvement on many of the historical responses to biodiversity loss that have sought to isolate humans from nature through elitist exclusion. Likewise, the narrative of "ecosystem services" that has become closely connected with NC contains ecological truths regarding our interrelationship with nature. There are ecological approaches to societal problems that could "save" money and enhance livelihoods. For example, protection and restoration of sub-tropical habitats such as mangrove forests would protect coastal settlements from flooding and maintain vital nursing grounds for tropical fisheries.

But the difficulty remains that various arms of capitalist industry have been, and are being, developed to exploit the self-made environmental problems of the system — most agribusiness operations are geared towards replacing natural ecology with artificial fertilisers and pesticides — and that these operate on shorter business cycles and vastly greater rates of profit than the "ecosystem services" that are derived from biodiversity or nature.

Although NC appears as a sophisticated, rigorous and holistic attempt to marry ecology with economics, "intellectual separation between economics and ecology" is in reality exactly what the approach entails. In place of critical analysis based on holistic socio-ecology, NC throws a net of economic simplicity and ideology over nature in its entirety. It seeks to identify the "true costs" of environmental degradation and conservation but its advocates have restricted themselves to an appallingly narrow spectrum of economic theory in order to demonstrate nature's worth.

The branches of economics that have been utilised — an unholy alliance of neoclassical and neoliberal doctrines — are so deeply enmeshed with bourgeois perspectives on economic respectability that NC advocates have somehow failed to notice that these are the very same schools of economics that have driven the biodiversity crisis while normalising our collective alienation from nature — the fundamental driving force behind the loss of biodiversity and associated human cultural diversity.

The outcomes of NC are therefore the exact opposite of what it proposes. Appealing to market capitalism, its corporations and politicians, to value biodiversity through money is akin to asking the fox to look after the henhouse. The situation is made even more perilous by the way in which NC has moved from being a technical method of environmental economics engaging in stocks and flows analysis to become a substitute for the concept of "nature" itself.[27]

If the development of NC is considered from the broader economic perspective that Williams subscribed to — one embedded in historical materialism — then three possible interpretations of this unfortunate turn in environmental history can be explored: natural capital as fictitious commodity; as primitive accumulation and as disaster capitalism.

Natural capital as "fictitious commodity"

NC represents an explicit attempt to assign economic value to biodiversity and ecosystems — entities that have failed to appear on the balance sheets of capitalism because they are viewed as market externalities or public (free) goods. But there remains a substantial problem with a valuation exercise that compares or meshes the value of currently free services with those generated, and therefore already transformed into commodities, by human labour.

27. I am grateful to Professor Sian Sullivan at Bath Spa University for this observation.

The chief problem is derived from the competitive market atmosphere into which ecosystem valuation is placed. Typically, for example, TEEB calculates that the total economic value of the Charles River Basin in Massachusetts is the equivalent of $95.5 million per annum (see table 1).[28]

Table 1: The economic value of the Charles River Basin

Economic benefit	Economic value per year (converted to US dollars)
Flood damage prevention	39,986,788
Amenity value of living close to the wetland	216,463
Pollution reduction	24,634,150
Recreation value: small game hunting, waterfowl hunting	23,771,954
Recreation value: trout fishing, warm water fishing	6,877,696
Total	95,487,051

This value is calculated from, "the benefits derived from these wetlands [including] flood control, amenity values, pollution reduction, water supply and recreational values".[29] Since a proportion of this value is calculated from market prices (the housing market element of "amenity value of living close to the wetland") then the wetlands' total value can rise and fall in line with non-ecological factors. A leisure or tourism contribution to ecosystem valuation is similarly problematic since it depends ultimately on the wetland's ability to compete with other leisure or tourist attractions, as well as an assumption that workers can maintain leisure expenditure despite booms and busts within the wider economy. In Costa Rica — the country often portrayed as the model for NC and PES — some ecologists have gone so far as to argue that rainforests should effectively be seen as farms for ecotourism and that the number of tourists visiting a rainforest reserve (and their associated tourist dollars) should be seen as the rainforest's crop!

A certain proportion of ecosystem valuation is, by implication,

28. TEEB, *The Economics of Ecosystems and Biodiversity,* as above, p383.
29. TEEB, as above, p383.

derived from within the existing capitalist system — for the Charles River Basin wetlands, roughly a third of their economic value is derived from existing fluctuating monetary cycles (the dollars spent on amenity and leisure). The remaining values that are applied relate to the ability of ecosystems to supply a monetary-equivalent service to humanity (flood damage prevention and pollution reduction). But these figures are similar to "fictitious capital" — "money that is thrown into circulation as capital without any material basis in commodities or productive activity"[30] — because they are applied as arbitrary values against an anthropogenic equivalent that would necessarily be derived through labour. If the value of an ecological function is only compared to how much it would cost humans to adopt technological measures were we to undertake the same "service", then a Marxist perspective shows how this comparison makes only limited sense. The latter would be determined by the quantity of human labour, not by any non-human ecological quality.

Further, where this comparison has played out on the ground the results have been unpredictable. Pollination is a much-lauded ecosystem service that is rightly highlighted by environmentalists as a deep and growing challenge as industrial pesticides have decimated species of bees and other invertebrates across the world. Hanyuan County, in China's Sichuan province, is noted for its fruit production — in particular its pear orchards. Over the last decade the region has suffered a pollination crisis as bee populations have crashed through historic use of pesticides. In the face of this crisis, farmers turned to human labour and much of the annual crop has now become dependent on pollination by hand — a process whereby pollen is dusted onto blossom by labourers. In the early phase of this crisis, although beehives could be rented to achieve the same outcome, farmers used workers to replace bees because labour costs were low and productivity increased as the human eye proved to be more effective. The crisis has recently returned

30. David Harvey, *The Limits to Capital* (Verso, 2006), p95.

as poor rural workers have migrated towards urban areas under industrialisation. As this example hints, once valued and embedded within the capitalist system, ecosystem services and its NC basis could be outcompeted by technological advances or other human attributes. In this regard, the possibilities of over-valuation and undervaluation through the desires and whims of speculative capitalist investors is also very real.

NC can also be described as a form of fictitious capital because its concern with realising monetary value for ecosystems through PES is effectively a form of ground rent. David Harvey argues that rent itself is a fictitious commodity, and that Karl Marx saw such as a sign of capitalism's insanity.[31]

Natural capital as "primitive accumulation"

Capitalism's historic ability to secure value from without was described by both Marx and Rosa Luxemburg as "primitive accumulation". While the privatisation and direct appropriation of communal resources such as land played a historical role in early capitalist expansion, certain aspects of this strategy appear to function today in the guise of "accumulation by dispossession".[32] In the Third World, dispossession of peasants' landholdings to service the needs of international commodity markets in "cash crops" has accelerated under neoliberalism since the 1970s — a trend continuous with colonial and post-colonial patterns of land use.[33]

NC appears to enhance this characteristic through its growing link to international agreements and legal structures that will

31. Harvey, The Limits to Capital, as above.

32. David Harvey, The New Imperialism (Oxford University Press, 2003); Chris Harman, "Theorising Neoliberalism", International Socialism 117, winter 2008, http://isj.org.uk/theorising-neoliberalism/; Jim Glassman, "Neoliberal Primitive Accumulation", in Nik Heynen, James McCarthy, Scott Prudham and Paul Robbins (eds), Neoliberal Environments: False Promises and Unnatural Consequences, Routledge, 2007; Sam Ashman and Alex Callinicos, "Capital Accumulation and the State System: Assessing David Harvey's The New Imperialism", Historical Materialism, volume 14, issue 4, 2006.

33. Harman, "Theorising Neoliberalism", as above; Rappel and Thomas, "An Examination of the Compatibility of World Bank Policies towards Population, Development and Biodiversity in the Third World", as above.

permit the development of property rights over ecological entities and functions. The transformation of public goods into property rights has the potential further to alienate humanity from its ecological base. In practice, this could arise through the impact of enclosure of formerly open resources through legislation or through illegal or discounted land grabbing.[34] As previously mentioned, such acts have already carried controversial implications within biodiversity conservation where land has been enclosed for nature reserves by colonial powers.

The intention appears benign — formal ownership of an ecosystem by its human users and managers should facilitate payment for its maintenance in line with the value derived from its local, regional and global ecological services. However, the introduction of ownership rights can subject these beneficiaries to new pressures. For example, once an ecosystem is entered into the cash nexus, what is to stop other wealthier interests from buying up resources and ecological rights? What happens if the function of an ecosystem becomes dominated by the needs of one interest group associated with a particular ecosystem service over another? Fixed ownership rights are also difficult to predict over time because of the dynamism inherent within ecology: How can ecological dynamism operate where the rationale for conservation of an ecosystem or species may be fixed to a particular marketable outcome? What happens to market value when an ecosystem changes its characteristic from within? These questions are generally avoided by NC environmentalists. But the issues raised do hint at the potential discrepancies between ecological functions and valuation imperatives under capitalism, and the dangers of extending the frontier of capitalist accumulation across living nature itself.

34. Nancy Lee Peluso, "Enclosure and Privatisation of Neoliberal Environments", in Nik Heynen, James McCarthy, Scott Prudham and Paul Robbins (eds), *Neoliberal Environments: False Promises and Unnatural Consequences* (Routledge, 2007); Fred Pearce, *The Landgrabbers: The New Fight Over Who Owns the Earth* (Eden Project Books, 2012).

Natural capital as "disaster capitalism"

The rationale for NC is derived from the biodiversity crisis. This, in turn, has its historic roots in the evolution of human societies. But the greatest acceleration in environmental degradation and associated biodiversity loss has occurred over the last 300 years through the development of capitalism. Within this period, the last four decades have witnessed the most extensive rates of degradation as capitalism has forced its way into every nation state and an increasing share of human activities. The growing dominance of capitalism over human affairs has given rise to a situation where capitalist solutions are increasingly offered to those crises that have arisen from the system itself. In its most extreme responses, "disaster capitalism" has even used natural disasters and wars to further its neoliberal penetration into regions and nation states.[35]

The circular logic of capitalist solutions to capitalist crises is now so commonplace that many formerly radical environmentalists have given up on criticising the system in order to explore options for how environmental problems can be addressed by capitalist measures.[36] The tone of TEEB itself is almost incredulous when it comes to the objective concerns of conservation to protect biodiversity from capitalist development: "*Even today, more political emphasis is placed on protecting and isolating ecosystems from economic development and commodity markets, than on redefining and regulating the latter*".[37]

While NC carries the stated aim of protecting biodiversity, the tendency for capitalism to seek to profit from its own crises means that it could equally operate as a truly grandiose version of "disaster capitalism" — a neoliberal response to the Anthropocene — that generates profit opportunities from a crisis of geological proportions.

35. Naomi Klein, *The Shock Doctrine: The Rise of Disaster Capitalism* (Penguin, 2008).

36. See for examples: Jonathon Porritt, *Capitalism as if the World Matters* (Earthscan, 2005); Mark Lynas, *The God Species: How the Planet Can Survive the Age of Humans* (Fourth Estate, 2011); Juniper, *What Has Nature Ever Done For Us?*, as above.

37. TEEB, as above, p155 (emphasis added).

The tragedy of natural capital

All three of these radical interpretations of natural capital are connected by neoliberal conservationists' acceptance of markets and private property relations. In particular, NC proponents display enormous faith in privatisation as a solution to the degradation of environmental commons. This ideological position has its own creation myth in the form of Garrett Hardin's "Tragedy of the Commons" — principally a Malthusian argument but one that has been produced regularly over the last half century to argue against any communal or socialist solutions to environmental problems.[38] In Hardin's own words:

> The [tragedy] develops in this way. Picture a pasture open to all. It is to be expected that each herdsman will try to keep as many cattle as possible on the commons. Such an arrangement may work reasonably satisfactorily for centuries because tribal wars, poaching and disease keep the numbers of both man and beast well below the carrying capacity of the land... Once social stability becomes a reality...the inherent logic of the commons remorselessly generates tragedy...each man [becomes] locked into a system that compels him to increase his herd without limit — in a world that is limited. Ruin is the destination toward which all men rush, each pursuing his own best interest in a society that believes in the freedom of the commons. Freedom in a commons brings ruin to all.[39]

38. Garrett Hardin, "The Tragedy of the Commons", in Phillip Appleman (ed), *An Essay on the Principle of Population,* Thomas Robert Malthus (Norton, 1976 [1968]). Hardin's work, like that of the Reverend Thomas Robert Malthus, could be quite accurately described as a libel against humanity (to borrow Marx and Engels's phrase). However, unlike Malthus's *Essay on the Principle of Population*, Hardin's work has no redeeming features. The Essay was at least extremely influential in the development of Charles Darwin's and Alfred Russell Wallace's theory of natural selection. It is a source of some historical solace to think that Malthus's work went on to help establish one of the most important pillars of philosophical materialism (if only because he certainly would not have wanted that as a legacy!).

39. Hardin, "The Tragedy of the Commons", as above, pp235-236.

Hardin targets the need to control the "freedom to breed" in particular, but his theory (which has virtually no ascertainable accuracy because "commons" have been historically managed and sustained through cultural practices and are never left "open" in the sense that Hardin promotes) is more often used to justify the need to privatise commons to realise their value and thereby to conserve them. This embeds them within a market system (in line with neoclassical economic views).[40]

Helm and virtually all the natural capital converts that I have met in conservation use Hardin's work as their starting point and justification. On that basis alone the assumptions of NC are as borderline fraudulent as Hardin's bourgeois-friendly theory. Alas, the economists and ecologists now engaged with NC have been allowed to take this pseudoscience to the next level of academic and disciplinary respectability despite the efforts of Marxist critics such as Paul Burkett.[41]

Towards a socialist response

The uncritical promotion of NC by environmental conservationists is a tactic of profound self-defeat. By encouraging the financialisation of nature, these environmentalists are actively extending the frontier of capitalist commodification across the living earth. Whether their motivations are derived from well-meaning pragmatism or neoliberal ideology, they will find that the crudeness of their efforts will backfire. In place of greater value-realisation for Earth's wonderful biodiversity, a crude lexicon of dumbed-down ecosystem services will come to the fore. Pro-development initiatives such as biodiversity

40. For excellent critiques and counter-blasts to Hardin's lazy theory I would recommend reading Ian Angus's 2008 essay for *Monthly Review Online* (Ian Angus, "The Myth of the Tragedy of the Commons", *Monthly Review Online*, 25 August 2008. *https://mronline.org/2008/08/25/the-myth-of-the-tragedy-of-the-commons/)* and Stefano N Longo, Rebecca Clausen and Brett Clark, *The Tragedy of the Commodity: Oceans, Fisheries and Aquaculture* (Rutgers University Press, 2015).

41. Paul Burkett, *Marxism and Ecological Economics: Toward a Red and Green Political Economy* (Brill, 2006).

offsetting[42] are already riding on the coat-tails of this commod-ification. And the much-hyped "new innovative markets" will merely promote Payments for Ecosystem Services, further enriching wealthy landowners and encouraging land grabbing and dispossession. Already, a new group of technocratic ecolo-gists is emerging to promote and exploit the pseudoscience of NC, offering enhanced monetary and political power for large NGOs and ecological consultancies, and a corresponding disen-franchisement of the public body and vulnerable groups such as small farmers and indigenous people.

Natural capital is potentially dangerous and its advocates must be vigorously challenged, despite the fact that they have normalised the concept within international politics and envi-ronmental discourse. At best, the concept is a hopelessly inef-fective means to reverse the sixth extinction because it repre-sents little more than another capitalist solution to a capitalist crisis. At worst, it provides the basis for commodifying, priva-tising and trading in living nature — developing new markets based on our current system of speculation and profit that will corrupt and distort ecology for short-term aims — leading to further biodiversity loss.

In place of capitulation to commodification, environmen-talists would better serve the interests of biodiversity if they subscribed to Harvey's observation: "We have loaded upon nature, often without knowing it, in our science as in our poetry, much of the alternative desire for value to that implied by money".[43] The struggle for alternative non-monetary, valua-tion is a central theme within socialism and other anti-capitalist traditions. It is an expression of resistance against the barbarism unleashed by capitalist valuation in all areas of human affairs, from ecology to education, from science to the arts. Appreciation

---

42. "Biodiversity offsetting" is the means by which capitalist developers, states and consultant ecologists assign scores for ecological damage within an agreed matrix of habitat type, species presence and quality. These scores are then given a monetary value with the aim of creating equivalent habitats elsewhere once the area under development has been destroyed. The concept is, unsurprisingly, mired in controversy.

43. David Harvey, *The Ways of the World* (Profile Books, 2016), p174.

of the need to fight for environmental quality over the quantitative world of the cash nexus helps us to consider our historic function and relevance as socialist ecologists. In those respects, we must fight for biodiversity today with a view to enhancing its recovery tomorrow. Whether the future is bound by ongoing and decaying capitalism, or is thrown open by meaningful revolution, we can operate today in the interests of all life on Earth once we accept and advocate certain radical conclusions.

First, that capitalism is ecologically dysfunctional and inherently destructive of biodiversity. Second, that dominant, neoliberal misanthropic explanations of the biodiversity crisis are fatalistic and cynical regarding humanity's historical and future interrelationship with biodiversity. And that the solutions (natural capital, neo-Malthusianism, the "tragedy of the commons", "clearance rewilding", the privatisation of nature reserves) flowing from these positions are also largely ideological and pro-capital.

Biodiversity conservation under prevailing capitalism is a "spaces of hope" project. Through various tools within the reformist armoury, we need to save what we can with meagre resources in the limited time available to us. These tools will also provide vital ecological lessons for the historically viable mode of society that will be derived through socialism. Some tools are socially and ecologically imperfect and need to be improved because of their association with elitism (nature reserves and national parks). Others require direct community activism across diverse united fronts that can cross class boundaries and seek to utilise complex planning and legal frameworks (resisting developments like fracking, or motorway road schemes). Some are currently small in scale but have enormous potential if they could be scaled-up under a different mode of social reproduction (organic agriculture and agroecology). Some are emergency measures that are fundamentally unappealing but sadly necessary (rare species breeding programmes, seed banks and zoological gardens). Others are largely verbal and prone to ambiguity or abuse but can be useful campaigning tools for holding power to some account ("sustainable development" legislation).

Whatever tools we use, we are compelled to act today in favour of biodiversity and its positive human associations in very distressing circumstances. But by maintaining radical critique while deploying the tools to hand, and acting in solidarity with groups and classes that are closely entwined with biodiversity, we can also generate ecological optimism for the Anthropocene on the reasonable Marxist grounds that the seeds of future society are sown in the present.

***

Chapter 6
Food, Agriculture and Climate Change

Martin Empson

Scientific evidence of the deepening environmental crisis is growing.[1] Climate change is happening faster than scientific models had predicted. At the same time, we are seeing little, if any, action to reduce emissions. So it is not surprising that hundreds of thousands of people have taken to the streets. In Britain, as well as elsewhere, this movement has brought together wide social forces, from environmental campaigners and NGOs, to trade unions and left wing organisations.

Within this movement important debates are being raised about what needs to be done. The dominant tone of these discussions is left wing, epitomised by the popularity of Naomi Klein's book *This Changes Everything: Capitalism Versus the Climate*.[2] The book is in part a product of the environmental movement, particularly what she calls "Blockadia", movements that have

1. This article first appeared in *International Socialism* 152, autumn 2016. Thanks to Alex Callinicos, Esme Choonara, Sarah Ensor, Suzanne Jeffery, Ian Rappel and Camilla Royle for their comments on the original version. Where possible I have updated the statistics used and made some additions and changes to bring it up to date.

2. Naomi Klein, *This Changes Everything: Capitalism vs the Climate* (Penguin, 2015).

emerged out of resistance to attempts by fossil fuel corporations to build pipelines, extract shale gas and exploit tar sands. The book has also helped shape the movement itself, leading to debates among activists about the nature of capitalism and its fossil fuel imperative.

But other debates are re-emerging. One that has manifested with renewed force is the question of agriculture, food and climate change. On both the London and Paris climate demonstrations around the COP21 conference, activists organised blocs calling for veganism to become a significant part of the fight against climate change. These blocs were often marked by calls on other activists to change their personal lifestyles to "save the planet". In London several hundred vegan activists held placards with slogans including "Want to Change the Climate? Change Your Diet Go Vegan!" or "Vegan Diet will save the Planet". The Bristol-based vegan campaigning organisation Viva! produced placards reading "There's no such thing as a meat eating environmentalist". Such demands contrast with the slogans that have dominated the movement more recently, which demand large-scale state action on climate change, such as the call for "One Million Climate Jobs".[3]

This focus on animal farming has been dramatically fuelled by the popularity of the 2014 film *Cowspiracy: The Sustainability Secret*. Directed by activist Kip Andersen and filmmaker Keegan Kuhn, *Cowspiracy* has become enormously influential, and after it was updated by executive producer Leonardo DiCaprio and streamed online by Netflix, it has been watched many thousands of times. The 90-minute documentary argues that animal agriculture is responsible for 51 percent of global emissions and the systematic destruction of rainforests, as

3. Since this article was first published in 2016 *Cowspiracy* continues to be an influence. In January 2019 the Brazilian singer-songwriter Anitta made headlines by recommending it to her 33.7 million Instagram followers as part of an announcement that she was making lifestyle changes. Veganism has also become much more mainstream. In January 2019 in Britain Veganuary was widely observed and news outlets reported a dramatic rise in the number of vegan food launches, with major chains such as Greggs and McDonalds jumping on the bandwagon.

well as wider environmental problems. As the title suggests, it implies a conspiracy involving government bodies, agricultural corporations and environmental NGOs to avoid discussing the role of animal farming in the environmental crisis.

The conclusion of the film is that only a vegan lifestyle can save the planet. And this argument is entering the mainstream of the environmental movement, as one banner on the London March for Climate, Justice and Jobs had it, "The No 1 Cause of Climate Change is Animal Agriculture". Demands to reduce meat eating aren't limited to activists either, with governments and even the UN making similar calls.[4]

But by emphasising individual behavioural changes as a way of tackling climate change this approach fails to challenge the systemic problems with the food system under capitalism, which are the real source of the problem. *Cowspiracy* rightly highlights many problems with modern farming. Its focus, however, is not on the nature of agriculture under capitalism, but one particular aspect of it.[5]

Modern agriculture is enormously destructive to the environment. This is the result of a food system driven by profit and dominated by supermarkets and multinationals. As a result, the system causes enormous quantities of waste, and holds up a "Western diet" as the ideal. Consumers are then blamed for their bad food choices, with little regard for the context in which those choices are made.

The solution is not individual dietary changes, but a radical transformation of the food system itself. In this article I will explore the environmental impact of agriculture under capitalism, particularly its contribution to climate change. I hope this can strengthen the anti-capitalist aspect of the

4. Elaine Graham-Leigh, *A Diet of Austerity: Class, Food and Climate Change* (Zero Books, 2014), pp7-8.

5. It is worth noting that *Cowspiracy* doesn't mentions any agricultural corporations, nor does it investigate food production outside of the United States so there is no attempt to discuss the question of livestock agriculture in the developing world, or the role of animals (such as for ploughing or transport) in agriculture outside of their use for meat, milk and eggs.

climate movement, and in turn the wider revolutionary challenge to capitalism.[6]

Agriculture and climate change

Cowspiracy's headline figure is that "livestock and their by-products account for ... 51 percent of all worldwide greenhouse gas [GHG] emissions". This figure is based on a report for the Worldwatch Institute by Robert Goodland and Jeff Anhang who argue that:

> The life cycle and supply chain of domesticated animals raised for food have been vastly underestimated as a source of GHGs...replacing livestock products with better alternatives would be the best strategy for reversing climate change. In fact, this approach would have far more rapid effects on GHG emissions and their atmospheric concentrations — and thus on the rate the climate is warming — than actions to replace fossil fuels with renewable energy.[7]

But these dramatic figures are contradicted by other studies. The United Nations Food and Agricultural Organisation (FAO) acknowledges that "the livestock sector plays an important role in climate change" but suggests that the emissions figure is much lower. In their 2013 report, *Tackling Climate Change Through Livestock: A Global Assessment of Emissions and Mitigation Opportunities,* the FAO argue that livestock represents 14.5 percent of human-induced

6. Because this chapter focuses on the question of agriculture and climate change, some of the wider debates are only touched on or omitted entirely. Some recommendations for further reading are included at the end of this book.

7. Robert Goodland, and Jeff Anhang, "Livestock and Climate Change", *World Watch Magazine*, volume 22, number 6, November-December, 2009, p11. *www.worldwatch.org/node/6294*

GHG emissions.[8] This is a reduction on an earlier study by the FAO, which concluded that livestock was responsible for 18 percent of GHG emissions.[9] The earlier study was considered flawed by some as it compared the full life-cycle of the livestock sector (including transport emissions, for example) with only a partial life-cycle for other sectors. Even though this was acknowledged by the authors of the later FAO report, the flawed figures of the 2006 report are still quoted by the makers of *Cowspiracy*.[10]

Danny Chivers, author and lead external carbon analyst for Christian Aid and ActionAid, has dismissed *Cowspiracy*'s figures:

> The 51 percent number comes from a single non-peer-reviewed report by two researchers — a report littered with statistical errors. This study counts the climate impact of methane from animals as being more than three times more powerful as methane from other sources, adds in an inappropriate chunk of extra land use emissions and incorrectly includes all the carbon dioxide that livestock breathe out.[11]

But acknowledging the limitations of the *Cowspiracy* figure is not to downplay the significance of livestock, or agriculture in general, for climate change. In the UK, for instance, government

8. Pierre Gerber, Henning Steinfeld, Benjamin Henderson, Anne Mottet, Carolyn Opio, Jeroen Dijkman, Alessandra Falcucci and Giuseppe Tempio, *"Tackling Climate Change Through Livestock: A Global Assessment of Emissions and Mitigation Opportunities"*, FAO, 2013, pxii. *www.fao.org/ag/againfo/resources/en/publications/tackling_climate_change/index.htm*

9. Henning Steinfeld, Pierre Gerber, Tom Wassenaar, Vincent Castel, Mauricio Rosales, Cees de Haan, *"Livestock's Long Shadow: Environmental Issues and Options"*, UN Food and Agriculture Organisation, November 2006, *www.fao.org/docrep/010/a0701e/a0701e00.HTM*

10. The FAO's acknowledgement of "methodological refinements and improved data" is in Gerber and others, "Tackling Climate Change Through Livestock", p15. See Robert Paarlberg *Food Politics: What Everyone Needs to Know* (Oxford University Press, 2013), p132 for more on the limits of the 2006 FAO report. The "flawed" figures are still quoted at *www.cowspiracy.com/facts/*

11. Danny Chivers, *"Cowspiracy: Stampeding in the Wrong Direction?"*, *New Internationalist Blog*, February 2016, *http://tinyurl.com/gm665so*

figures show that agriculture is responsible for 10 percent of total GHG emissions; 32 percent of this is nitrous oxide and 57 percent methane emissions and the remainder carbon dioxide.[12] Methane is a significant greenhouse gas with a warming impact 23 times greater than carbon dioxide. It originates from a number of sources, such as the decomposition of organic material, but is particularly important in livestock farming because animals such as cattle, sheep, goats, pigs and buffalo produce large quantities as part of their digestion. Methane is also emitted when animal manure is stored to be used as fertiliser. Nitrous oxide is emitted mostly through the use of synthetic fertilisers.

In March 2014, the FAO produced figures showing that in 2011 global agricultural emissions were the highest in history, 5,335 megatonnes of CO_2 equivalent (about 9 percent higher than the average for the preceding decade), and are projected to increase by 30 percent by 2050.[13] The Intergovernmental Panel on Climate Change (IPCC) estimates that global emissions from agriculture, forestry and other land use are around 24 percent of the world's total.[14] A 2012 study argues that food systems as a whole contribute between 19 and 29 percent of GHG emissions, of which 80 to 86 percent is from agriculture.[15]

Agriculture is a large contributor to climate change for three main reasons. Firstly, an increasing part of agriculture is the growing of crops to produce feed for animals and biofuels.

12. Total UK emissions from agriculture in 2016 were 46.5 million tonnes of CO_2 equivalent. This is a decline of around 16 percent since 1990, "driven by a fall in animal numbers over the period, together with a decrease in synthetic fertiliser use." DEFRA, "2016 UK Greenhouse Gas Emissions, Final Figures", February 2018, *https://assets.publishing. service.gov.uk/government/uploads/system/uploads/attachment_data/file/680473/2016_ Final_Emissions_statistics.pdf*

13. F N Tubiello, M Salvatore, R D Cóndor Golec, A Ferrara, S Rossi, R Biancalani, S Federici, "Agriculture, Forestry and Other Land Use Emissions by Sources and Removals by Sinks", *UN Food and Agriculture Organisation*, March 2014, p20, p23. *www.fao.org/docrep/019/ i3671e/i3671e.pdf* "CO_2 equivalent" means the amount of CO_2 that would have the same warming effect.

14. IPCC, *Climate Change 2014: Mitigation of Climate Change, Fifth Assessment Report* (Cambridge University Press, 2014), p816. *www.ipcc.ch/report/ar5/wg3/*

15. Sonja J Vermeulen, Bruce M Campbell and John S I Ingram, "Climate Change and Food Systems", *Annual Review of Environment and Resources*, volume 37, 2012.

Secondly, agriculture is a significant cause of deforestation (71 percent of tropical deforestation between 2000 and 2012 was linked to clearances for cultivation[16]), and finally the whole of modern, industrialised agriculture is reliant on the use of fossil fuels.

The growing of crops is the conversion of nutrients from the soil and carbon dioxide from the atmosphere into plants that can be eaten. Some plants cannot be directly eaten by humans but can be consumed by animals, turning them into meat or milk, or giving them energy to pull a plough or transport materials. Since ancient times farmers have known that applying extra nutrients to soil can improve crop yields. Historically, animal manure has been used to do this, but from the 19th century onwards, as scientific understanding of chemical processes grew, the application of other fertilisers became common. At first this included sources of nutrients such as ground up bones or bird guano. But, as the industrial revolution developed, artificial fertilisers became the most common way of replenishing the soil. Today the manufacture of fertiliser requires enormous energy inputs from fossil fuels. In the developed world oil is also essential to the harvesting, ploughing and transport of crops and animals, and the food that they are processed into. Another significant use of fossil fuels is in the manufacture of pesticides that are used to kill weeds and insects.

The rising demand for meat and other products of the meat industry, such as milk, eggs or cheese, means that livestock farming has become enormous. The global population (2017) of chickens is calculated at 22.8 billion birds, while there are estimated to be 1.5 billion cattle, 1.2 billion sheep and 967 million pigs.[17]

Emissions from cattle farming are the single biggest emissions

16. Sam Jones, "Tropical Forests Illegally Destroyed for Commercial Agriculture", Guardian, 11 September 2014, http://tinyurl.com/lthlluv

17. FAO figures from http://faostat3.fao.org/home/E. In the original version of this article I used 2013 figures. It is worth noting that the intervening years saw an increase of 1.8 billion chickens, 500 million cattle and 100 million sheep. The number of pigs increased but then decreased to a slightly lower figure.

of livestock farming. Most of this comes from beef production (41 percent of total livestock emissions) with 20 percent coming from milk production. In some developing areas of the world, emissions from livestock used for transport or draught-power remain high — accounting for a quarter of emissions in South Asia and sub-Saharan Africa.[18] Environmentalists who argue that stopping climate change requires reducing numbers of cattle and buffalo rarely suggest an alternative to those communities who rely on animals for farming and transport.

The sheer scale of emissions from livestock farming is worth examining. Take the example of the South American beef industry. According to the FAO, this is responsible for 31 percent of the global beef sector. This contributes about 1 billion tonnes of CO_2 equivalent to GHG emissions. There are two main sources of emissions. Firstly, enteric fermentation, the digestive process by which micro-organisms in an animal's stomach break down food so it can be absorbed into the bloodstream, produces methane (which, for the South American beef industry, is responsible for 30 percent of emissions). Secondly, the use of manure as fertiliser and land-use change — such as deforestation to expand grazing areas — contribute to emissions by 23 percent and 40 percent respectively.[19]

Even under the existing system there is potential for significant reductions in emissions. But these will often require technological improvements or changes to agricultural practices, so may be rejected by companies that are unwilling to reduce profits or farmers who lack the capital to introduce them. But they do demonstrate the way a food system that is driven by need, not by profit, could reduce emissions. For instance, the FAO notes that emissions from the livestock sector could be reduced by 18 percent by generalising from the best practices of those with the lowest emissions and by utilising existing technologies, but this is dependent on "conducive policies and market signals"

18. Gerber and others, "Tackling Climate Change Through Livestock", as above, p23.
19. Gerber and others, as above, pp68-69.

existing to encourage the adoption of these best practices.[20] The FAO also notes that reducing deforestation, reducing the expansion of agricultural areas and improving how and where animals are grazed could also lead to the further sequestration of greenhouse gases in soil (some 409 million tonnes of CO_2 equivalent per year). Other practices, such as the sowing of legumes (plants such as peas, clover and beans) on grassland, can significantly improve the ability of the soil to absorb carbon.[21]

Concern about emissions from agriculture is not simply their impact on the environment; emissions also reflect inefficiencies in the agricultural process itself. For example, animal feed is often the most expensive part of livestock farming, and methane emissions represent a waste of the energy input in the form of feed. Therefore reducing emissions can also reduce farming costs through energy reduction in the food system.[22]

Emissions from livestock agriculture vary dramatically from region to region, often reflecting different types of farming, or land use in the particular region. For instance, globally, land use change is responsible for 15 percent of the beef industry's emissions, but for chicken production it is 21 percent. This is because land use change originates in deforestation for beef, but for chickens it is related to the production of their soybean feed. This creates a further difficulty in estimating industry emissions, because soybeans are traded internationally so their emissions are attributed in different locations worldwide, but deforestation emissions are considered locally.[23] There is also enormous variety between countries reflecting different industrial practices.[24] But broadly speaking, agriculture in the most affluent areas of the globe has high emissions when measured against the land area. But the emissions per unit of agricultural production are low.[25]

20. Gerber and others, as above, p46.
21. As above, pp50-51.
22. As above, p40.
23. As above, p41.
24. As above, p42.
25. As above, p53.

Production methods can also affect the level of emissions per unit of production. There is a strong negative correlation between the amount of milk produced by cows and emission intensity. In other words, as yield increases, the amount of emissions per unit of production decreases. There are three reasons for this, with implications for reducing total emissions from farming. The first is that as total yields grow, emissions are spread over a larger amount of production. Secondly, improvements in productivity (such as the use of different feeds, mechanised milking machines or drugs to improve production) are often related to improved technologies and practices that can also reduce emissions. Finally, improvements to herd management, as well as animal health and husbandry, "increase the proportion of resources utilised for productive purposes rather than simply being used to maintain the animals".[26]

The use of technology can help reduce both total emissions and the amount of emissions per unit of production at least in some areas of livestock agriculture, such as milk production. Because the amount of methane cows produce varies naturally, current research suggests that selective breeding could mean future animals may be less polluting than currently, even without using extra technologies.[27]

OECD countries have only 20 percent of the global dairy cows, but produce 73 percent of the world's milk. Average emissions for OECD milk production are thus much lower than the world in general. The FAO's case study of this sector suggests that "feasible improvements in manure management, energy use, feed quality and animal performance" could lead to reductions of between 14 and 17 percent of GHGs (which is between 4 and 5 percent of the emissions from the global milk sector). The exact way of doing this would depend on regional factors — in Western Europe better energy use is the most significant factor,

26. As above, p42.

27. Martin Ince, "The Case for Low Methane-emitting Cattle", 10 January 2014, *http://tinyurl.com/z7b3a7j*. I am indebted to John Parrington for pointing this out to me.

while in North America "wider use of anaerobic digesters" to break down animal waste is suggested.[28]

But with agriculture, as with other sectors such as energy generation or transport, we have to be wary of simply seeing either technology or particular production methods as necessarily leading to lower emissions. For example, there are three types of chicken production: backyard layers, industrial layers and industrial broilers. The first two produce meat and eggs, the third only meat. Industrial broiler and egg farming has the lowest emission intensity for similar reasons to that of milk production in cows. Chickens running free in a backyard have high emission intensity per egg as the animals grow more slowly and produce fewer eggs, their feed tends to be of lower quality, and the ratio of unproductive to productive animals is higher than in industrial production. So industrial poultry production produces less energy emissions per unit than backyard farming.

However, we must be careful not to lose sight of the wider context. Although industrial poultry farming results in fewer emissions, there are other negatives. Chickens are frequently kept in terrible conditions and live short, often painful lives, with a high usage of antibiotics and other drugs to encourage rapid growth. The use of drugs to produce cheap meat may well have health impacts for consumers. Mass poultry farming is also unhealthy for those who work in the industry — a US Bureau of Labor Statistics report showed that the poultry industry has one of the highest levels of occupational illness.[29] US poultry farming is dominated by a few massive corporations that contract out chicken growing to smaller farms (while the animals themselves remain the property of the corporation). This leads to farmers being trapped in an unequal relationship, at the beck and call of the businesses solely motivated by profits.[30]

28. Gerber and others, as above, pp76-78.
29. Philip Lymbery, *Farmageddon: The True Cost of Cheap Meat* (Bloomsbury, 2014), p193.
30. For more on the industrial chicken, see Lymbery, *Farmageddon*, as above, pp187-196.

But when we consider the emissions from pig farming, the "difference in emission intensities between the various production systems is not substantial". While the majority of total emissions from the pig sector still come from industrial farming, emissions are similar when considered against backyard production. The reason for this is mostly linked to the lower quality of food given to backyard animals (often waste from other sources), which means lower emissions.[31] So it is not automatic that switching to industrialised farming, or to highly technological practices will reduce emissions.

I will return to strategies to reduce emissions later. But for now it's worth noting two conclusions. Firstly, there is a large potential to reduce emissions from agriculture and particularly livestock farming. The use of improved technology and other practices can, in certain circumstances, have a significant impact on the amount of emissions. I have already noted the FAO conclusion that emissions could be reduced by between 18 and 30 percent if producers in particular regions were all able to take up the practices used by the 10 to 25 percent of producers who have the lowest emissions.

Secondly, emissions reductions can be achieved in both the developed and developing world, but the methods may vary. High emissions from industrialised farming might be better achieved through "on-farm efficiency, such as better manure management and energy saving devices" but elsewhere better land management, herd management and changes to feeding practices are needed.[32] There is no one size fits all solution to reducing emissions from agriculture, rather a wide variety of answers.

How climate change affects agriculture
Finally, it's worth highlighting how climate change will impact on agriculture. It used to be commonly thought that global warming would be beneficial to farmers, as higher carbon

31. Gerber and others, as above, pp35-36.
32. As above, p44.

dioxide levels would act as a fertiliser and improve crop yields. While this is true (yields of some crops, such as wheat, can rise by 30 percent if CO_2 doubles), any improvement also depends on other factors such as nutrient levels, water availability and average temperatures.

Fish and shellfish are highly vulnerable to temperature changes, and increasing acidification of the oceans will further impact on already low stocks. This in turn can have a further negative impact on agriculture as something like a third of the world's fish catch ends up as animal feed. The practice of feeding farm animals and fish on other fish and krill from the oceans is also significantly damaging to the ocean's ecosystems.

Extreme weather events, such as droughts and floods, are likely to become more intense and frequent as the world warms. Since agriculture is often concentrated in particular regions, this can lead to major risks to crop production. For instance, a third of all wheat, corn and rice that is traded internationally originates in the United States. In 2012 America experienced its worst drought since 1950 with 60 percent of US farms experiencing moderate to extreme drought in August. As a result, corn production was down to 2006 levels and export prices rose by 33 percent in the summer.[33] In 2018 in the UK weeks of warm weather and lack of rain led to falling yields and shortages of vegetable crops such as carrots, lettuce, onions, and cauliflower. Other crops suffered as some pests thrive in warmer weather.

The melting of glaciers also threatens agriculture. In the Himalayas some 15,000 glaciers feed about half the Brahmaputra, Ganges and Indus rivers' annual flow. As those glaciers melt there will be an initial surge in water levels, but a warming world ultimately threatens a billion people who rely on the rivers' water. In South America, Andean glaciers supply water

---

33. Will Adonizio, Nancy Kook and Sharon Royales, "Impact of the Drought on Corn Exports: Paying the Price", *Beyond the Numbers*, US Bureau of Labor Statistics, volume 1, number 17, 2012, p2. *www.bls.gov/opub/btn/volume-1/pdf/impact-of-the-drought-on-corn-exports-paying-the-price.pdf*

and hydroelectric energy to nearly 80 million people. In 2010 Henry Pollack wrote that "one quarter of Earth's population will within another few decades begin to be affected significantly by lesser snowfall and glacial ice loss".[34]

Climate change will hit agriculture and food in other ways. A US report, published in April 2016, highlights some of these. It suggests that some illnesses such as salmonella and e. coli will become more common in warmer weather and notes that higher carbon dioxide levels will reduce protein levels in food. The frightening conclusion is that extreme weather could interrupt food supply chains, will intensify pesticide use in reaction to changing insect populations and will lower concentrations of essential minerals such as iron and zinc in food.[35]

The wider environmental impact of agriculture

Historically, agriculture has been the most significant way in which humans have altered their environment. The emergence of agriculture around 10,000 years ago can be linked to a wide variety of environmental and ecological changes. These have included deforestation, changes to water courses for irrigation and the selective breeding of plants and animals for domestication. Under capitalism, like earlier human societies, we continue to alter the environment and agriculture forms a significant part of this process. But the nature of production under capitalism has meant the transformation of nature has been taken to a new level. John Bellamy Foster, Brett Clark and Richard York have described how Karl Marx developed an understanding of the way that capitalism created a "metabolic rift" in the "exchange between humanity and nature":

> The context was the robbing of the soil of the countryside of nutrients and the sending of these nutrients to the cities in the form of food and fibre, where they ended

34. Henry Pollack, *A World Without Ice* (Penguin, 2010), pp200-202.
35. USGCRP, *The Impacts of Climate Change on Human Health in the United States: A Scientific Assessment* (US Global Change Research Program, 2016).

up contributing to pollution. This rupture in the soil nutrient cycle undermined the regenerative capacities of the ecosystem. Marx argued that it was necessary to "restore" the soil metabolism to ensure environmental sustainability for the generations to come.[36]

This rift has its origins in a system of production that treats the natural world only as part of the productive process itself, a source of raw materials or energy, or a dump for the waste of that productive process. While no agricultural production can fail to have an impact upon nature, the industrialised farming that currently dominates produces, in Marx's words, "an irreparable rift in the interdependent process of social metabolism".[37]

The almond industry presents a stark example of this. Some 80 percent of the world's almonds come from highly intensive farms in Central Valley, California. Around 60 million almond trees are planted in orchards covering 240,000 hectares of land. The area has so little rain it is classified as "semi-desert". In addition to almonds there are giant dairies and huge fields of fruit, nuts and vegetables. In *Farmageddon*, Philip Lymbery describes this as:

> a deeply disturbing place where not a blade of grass, no tree or hedgerow grows, except in private gardens and the ruthlessly delineated fields. The phenomenal output of fruit and veg is possible only thanks to a cocktail of chemicals and the plundering of the crystal-clear rivers that run down from the Sierra Nevada mountains...farmers have been able to pull off a multi-billion-dollar conjuring trick, extracting harvests from soil that is so depleted of natural matter it might as well be brown polystyrene.[38]

36. John Bellamy Foster, Brett Clark and Richard York, *The Ecological Rift: Capitalism's War on the Earth* (Monthly Review Press, 2010), p46

37. Karl Marx, *Capital, vol. 3* (Penguin, 1992), p949.

38. Lymbery, *Farmageddon*, as above, p13.

Industrialised agriculture like this means there are no longer enough bees to pollinate the crops, so every year 3,000 lorries carry 40 billion bees across the United States to California where they pollinate the almond trees at a cost of $250 million a year.[39]

Honeybees, central to the production of food, are themselves victims of industrial farming. Colony collapse disorder has been linked to pesticides called neonicotinoids, but other factors are closely linked to industrial farming. For instance, in Central Valley hedges and unploughed field margins where bees might have lived have been removed to create giant orchards. More problematically, these mono-cropped areas rely on the heavy use of artificial fertilisers. Historically farmers allowed soils to replenish themselves through crop rotation — leaving a field fallow, or sowing a crop such as clover, which also encourages bees. But large-scale, monocropped industrial farming simultaneously reduces food sources and poisons and destroys the places where bees live.[40]

One Indian ecologist, Dr Parthiba Basu, argues that declining forests and increased pesticide use are key factors in the collapse of bee populations:

I had hoped that pollinator loss would not be nearly as serious in developing countries as it is in the West, but that does not seem to be the case. It is very sad. It is going to take a lot of effort to turn this around, but unfortunately the developing world is going down the opposite route right now, embracing Western-style intensification. That means more mono-cropping and chemical fertiliser and pesticide use, and more loss of the wilderness habitats on which bees depend.[41]

39. Lymbery, as above, pp63-64.

40. Lymbery, as above, p68.

41. Tom Philpott, "Are Your Delicious, Healthy Almonds Killing Bees?" *Mother Jones,* 29 April 2014, *www.motherjones.com/tom-philpott/2014/04/california-almond-farms-blamed-honeybee-die*

But using industrially bred bees in vast quantities is not a fail-safe solution. In 2014 between 15 and 25 percent of beehives brought to California for almond pollination were severely damaged, leading to the death of millions of bees. It seems likely that the cause was the use of new "adjuvants", chemicals used to improve the efficiency of pesticides but which make hitherto safe pesticides lethal to bees. So the almond industry has created and become dependent on a bee industry, but the farming practices used also threaten the viability of the bee industry itself. There can be no better example of the "metabolic rift" in modern agriculture.[42]

Karl Marx might have been writing about the almond and bee industries when he commentated about capitalist farming:

> Agriculture no longer finds the natural conditions of its own production within itself, naturally, arisen, spontaneous, and ready to hand, but these exist as an independent industry separate from it — and, with this separateness the whole complex set of interconnections in which this industry exists is drawn into the sphere of the conditions of agricultural production.[43]

The almond industry also highlights another important environmental aspect of farming — the question of water. Growing crops and animals requires vast quantities of water. Some 3,400 litres of water are needed to grow a kilogram of rice, 3,900 for a kilogram of chicken and between 15,000 and 100,000 litres for a kilogram of beef.[44] A single almond requires slightly over 4 litres of water.[45]

A hectare of "high-yield" rice needs about 11 million litres

42. I am indebted to Adam Rose for this point.

43. John Bellamy Foster and Brett Clark, 2016, "Marx's Ecology and the Left", *Monthly Review*, June 2016, *http://monthlyreview.org/2016/06/01/marxs-ecology-and-the-left/*

44. Paul McMahon, *Feeding Frenzy: The New Politics of Food* (Profile, 2013), p89.

45. Tom Philpott, "Your Almond Habit is Sucking California Dry", *Mother Jones*, 14 July 2014, *www.motherjones.com/tom-philpott/2014/07/your-almond-habit-sucking-califoirnia-dry*

to produce 7 tons of rice. Soybeans require about 5.8 million litres to get three tons per hectare. Wheat uses "only" about 2.4 million litres for 2.7 tons per hectare. Vandana Shiva has pointed out that these high-yield seeds should really be known as "high-response" varieties as they require such increased inputs in the form of chemicals and water.[46] Growing crops using irrigation as opposed to rainwater alone requires three times more energy to grow the same amount of grain, adding to the GHG emissions.[47]

Agriculture is helping to rapidly deplete freshwater reserves, particularly underground aquifers. Some wells are replenished naturally, but others, known as fossil aquifers, hold water that has been there for thousands of years and is not replenished. In the United States the Ogallala aquifer provides about 30 percent of irrigation water used by the country's farmers, and it may dry up within 25 years.[48] The deeper or more inaccessible the water, the more energy must be expended in pumping it to the surface, which means more fossil fuels being burnt, increasing emissions. The World Bank estimates that 175 million people in India and 130 million in China depend on grain produced by over-pumping.[49]

Agriculture also causes pollution of rivers, lakes and the sea. One cause of this is the pollution from animal manure. Britain's animals annually produce 80 million tons of manure. In Britain an "average-sized dairy herd of a hundred cows can produce as much effluent as a town of 5,000 people. Across the country there are a total of 1.8 million dairy cows, not to mention many millions of pigs, chickens and other farm animals".[50] In the past manure from cows was spread back on the fields as fertiliser, but intensive dairy farming (or factory farming of chickens and

46. Vandana Shiva, *The Vandana Shiva Reader* (Kentucky University Press, 2014), p222.

47. Fred Magdoff and Brian Tokar, *Agriculture and Food in Crisis: Conflict, Resistance, and Renewal* (Monthly Review Press, 2010), p243.

48. McMahon, *Feeding Frenzy*, as above, p66.

49. McMahon, as above, p66.

50. Lymbery, *Farmageddon*, as above, p172.

pigs) produces such vast quantities of manure that it cannot possibly be spread on the soil. Some is stored in vast pools, and leakages can pollute groundwater and emit gases into the air.[51] Lymbery quotes Kevin Hamilton, a respiratory therapist in the previously described Central Valley on the impact of pollution from high-intensity farming:

> We're talking about heart disease, birth defects, and stunted lung development among children who spent a lot of time outside playing sport. We're talking about high blood pressure and increased risk of stroke. We have the second highest level of childhood asthma in the whole of the US.[52]

Some mega-dairies in the region have tens of thousands of cows.[53] The waste from these, plus the chemicals and pesticides used, is creating a health crisis. Hamilton continues: "You have to use a phenomenal amount of chemicals to push multiple crops out of the soil we have here... These pesticides are capable of penetrating the human body to genome level — meaning they can affect the very building blocks of the body".[54]

Leakages and rainfall can wash the manure into streams and rivers, and the amassed nutrients can lead to "dead zones" in water. Agriculture run-off from "excessive" fertiliser use on farms in the Mississippi watershed has caused a 6,000 square mile dead zone in the Gulf of Mexico no longer able to support life.[55]

In developed countries such as Britain and the US farmers' organisations have been able to organise to prevent government

51. Agriculture run-off in the UK is one of the major reasons why the UK is not expected to meet the Water Framework Directive well beyond the deadline of 2021.

52. Lymbery, *Farmageddon*, as above, p23.

53. China also has enormous cow factories. In July 2015 one was being built to house 100,000 cattle to supply milk and cheese to Russian markets. See *www.fwi.co.uk/livestock/china-building-100000-cow-dairy-unit-to-supply-russian-market.htm*

54. Lymbery, *Farmageddon*, as above, p24.

55. Paarlberg, *Food Politics*, as above, pp117-118.

action to reduce such pollution. In the US, "Congress does not regulate excess nitrogen runoff from farms and does not tax farm fertiliser use." Instead it pays farmers to temporarily leave land unused to reduce pollution. In other words, the government is paying the polluters, rather than punishing them for polluting. In one case, when Al Gore planned to tax sugar growers in Florida to fund a clean-up of the Everglades, a sugar baron simply telephoned then president Bill Clinton to cancel the tax plan.[56]

The human impact of pesticide use is not just limited to those living near to highly industrialised farms. In the developing world larger proportions of populations are engaged in agriculture, threatening more people. Plantation crops such as tea, cotton, coffee and vegetables are pesticide intensive and expose large areas and large numbers of people to the chemicals. The World Health Organisation estimates that 20,000 workers die from exposure to pesticides every year, most of them in the developing world.[57]

Pesticide use brings both benefits and potential problems. The "Green Revolution" of the 1970s saw crop yields dramatically increase as new strains of crops were developed. Alongside this, the use of pesticides increased, closely associated with higher government subsidies. Sometimes over-use of pesticides was associated with wider environmental destruction (as well as costs to human health). In Indonesia, for instance, in the early 1980s, massive government subsidies for fertilisers and pesticides led to excessive use on rice fields. As well as killing pests, over-use of pesticides also destroyed species that were essential to insect control (such as spiders). When "bad insects" such as planthoppers evolved pesticide resistance, the government had to intervene to ban 75 different insecticides allowing the recovery of insects to control the pests.[58]

56. Paarlberg, *Food Politics*, as above, pp127-128.

57. Imran Hashmi and Dilshad A Khan, "Adverse Health Effects of Pesticides Exposure in Agricultural and Industrial Workers of Developing Country", in Margarita Stoytcheva (ed), *Pesticides: The Impacts of Pesticide Exposure* (InTech, 2011), p161. *http://tinyurl.com/zjt94sw*

58. Paarlberg, *Food Politics*, as above, pp72-73.

One response to this has been for some farmers and consumers to turn to organic crops to reduce the use of artificial pesticides. Organic farming is an attempt to make agriculture more sustainable, biologically diverse and healthy by reducing the use of artificial chemicals. For example, methods such as crop rotation, manure and cover-crops are used to replenish the soil, rather than relying on artificial fertilisers.

This is an understandable reaction to industrialised farming, but again we should be wary of neglecting the very real benefits of technological improvements to agriculture as represented by the Green Revolution. For instance, in 1964 India produced 12 million tons of wheat on 14 million hectares; 30 years later production was 57 million tons from 24 million hectares. Calculations show that without the benefits of the Green Revolution, an additional 36 million hectares of farming land would have been needed. [59]Organic farming does not on its own prevent health dangers. In 2006 three people died and hundreds became ill as a result of e. coli infections from spinach grown on a Californian organic farm, nine died from salmonella linked to organic peanut plants in Texas and Georgia and in 2011 53 people died from e.coli after eating bean sprouts grown on a German organic farm.[60] Such examples suggest that the problem is not simply pesticides and the solution simply organic farming, but a whole range of processes in agriculture that can lead to health issues.

Because organic farming is less dependent on fossil fuels (used in the manufacture of artificial chemicals and pesticides), it can lead to significant reductions in overall greenhouse gas emissions. A 2006 report, for instance, concluded that if 10 percent of all US maize were grown organically, it could save 4.6 million barrels of oil. This can also be true of the meat industry. The Soil Association in the UK has calculated that organic milk

59. Paarlberg, *Food Politics*, as above, p73.
60. Paarlberg, as above, p173.

uses 38 percent less energy than non-organic; for beef the figures are 35 percent less, lamb 25 percent less.[61] But again we must be wary of seeing these figures out of context. A 2012 Oxford University report concluded that "organic systems were often better for the environment per unit of land, but conventional systems were often better per unit of production". This report also contradicted the Soil Association figures quoted above, suggesting that "organic milk, cereals, and pork production generated higher greenhouse gas emissions per unit of output than the conventional alternative".[62]

The key conclusion is that organic farming methods have much to offer from an environmental point of view. But benefits are not automatic, and depend on volume and scale, as well as the use of technology in a way that is designed to reduce environmental impacts. Colin Tudge, a British campaigner for "enlightened farming", argues that "organic farming need not be the absolute requirement… But it should be the default position: what farmers do unless there is a very good biological reason to do something else".[63]

In addition, animal agriculture has other impacts, not least to global biodiversity. As Sarah Ensor shows elsewhere in this book industrial farming is a major cause of this. Deforestation leads to a decrease in habitats and loss of species. Huge amounts of fish are caught to be used as animal feed — undermining species, and having a knock on effect on other sea-life. The heavy use of chemicals as pesticides have led to a massive decline in farmland birds — in Europe today there the number of birds has dropped by 300 million since 1980 with some species reduced by 90 percent or more. Philip Lymbery points that the problem isn't simply chemicals, but the nature of animal agriculture. Housing animals in enormous sheds means

61. Figures from, Lymbery, *Farmageddon*, as above, pp238-239.

62. Paarlberg, *Food Politics,* as above, p175. The Oxford University study is summarised at *www.ox.ac.uk/news/2012-09-04-organic-farms-not-necessarily-better-environment*

63. Colin Tudge, *Good Food for Everyone Forever: A People's Takeover of the World's Food Supply* (Pari Publishing, 2011), p68.

their food must be grown elsewhere, which encourages mono-cropping agriculture that destroys biodiversity.[64]

One final environmental and health impact of farming is particularly associated with the meat industry. The high use of antibiotics in industrial animal farming encourages the spread of antibiotic resistance in animals and humans. Some "80 percent of antibiotic use in America is on farms, 70 percent... to boost growth or prevent disease rather than to treat it".[65] Antibiotic use is particularly associated with factory farming, where the close confinement of animals provides the potential for disease to spread easily.

This heavy use of antibiotics is breeding resilience in the bacteria it is intended to destroy, which then enter the food chain or can spread to humans through manure, etc. Over half of Dutch pig farmers and 40 percent of Dutch pigs, for instance, carry a strain of pig-MRSA, and tests suggest it is present in 35 percent of raw meat in the Netherlands. In Britain in 2011, 15 cases of a new strain of MRSA were found in milk from British dairies. Factory farming and over-use of antibiotics are helping to create super-strains of diseases. One study of salmonella in British chickens found that smaller flocks and non-caged birds were less likely to carry the disease.[66] In 2010:

> Over 18 percent of caged flocks tested positive for salmonella enteritidis, the most common strain causing food poisoning, compared with less than 3 percent of non-caged flocks. The largest flocks of 30,000 birds or more were seven times more likely to carry salmonella than the smallest flocks of 3,000 hens or less.[67]

Viral diseases such as bird flu and swine flu are closely

64. See Philip Lymbery, "The Great Disappearing Act" in Joyce D'Silva and Carol McKenna, *Farming, Food and Nature* (Earthscan, 2018), pp15-16.

65. Lymbery, *Farmageddon*, as above, p139.

66. As above, pp144-145.

67. As above, p145.

associated with intensified farming for chickens and pigs, which provide perfect conditions for the evolution of new strains of these bugs. As Rob Wallace has commented, "the present agricultural model is farming tomorrow's deadliest pathogens alongside its meat monocultures".[68] There is no doubt that industrialised agriculture is a threat to the environment and to human health.[69] What has caused this to happen?

Agriculture under capitalism

Agriculture is closely associated with the rise of capitalism. Marx saw "the expropriation of the agricultural producer...from the soil"[70] as being key to the primitive accumulation that formed the basis for the development of capitalist society. This process created the basis for capitalist production, but also transformed the nature of agriculture and fuelled the growth of urban industry:

> The spoliation of the church's property, the fraudulent alienation of the State domains, the robbery of the common lands, the usurpation of feudal and clan property, and its transformation into modern private property under circumstances of reckless terrorism, were just so many idyllic methods of primitive accumulation. They conquered the field for capitalistic agriculture, made the soil part and parcel of capital, and created for the town industries the necessary supply of a "free" and outlawed proletariat.[71]

68. Rob Wallace, *Big Farms Make Big Flu* (Monthly Review Press, 2016), p130.

69. While this article focuses on agriculture, these conclusions are also true of the fishing industry. See Lymbery, *Farmageddon*, as above, chapter 5 and Sarah Ensor, "Two Books That Swim Against the Tide", *International Socialism* 150, spring 2016, http://isj.org.uk/two-books-that-swim-against-the-tide/

70. Karl Marx, *Capital, vol. 1* (Penguin, 1990), p876. See Kohei Saito, "The Emergence of Marx's Critique of Modern Agriculture: Ecological Insights from his Excerpt Notebooks", *Monthly Review*, October 2014, http://monthlyreview.org/2014/10/01/the-emergence-of-marxs-critique-of-modern-agriculture/ Saito's article is an important study of how Marx developed his understanding of capitalist agriculture in the context of contemporary scientific debates.

71. Marx, *Capital, vol. 1*, as above, p895.

Agriculture under capitalism is, like every other branch of production, shaped by the need for the capitalists to accumulate wealth for the sake of further accumulation. Space precludes a detailed overview of modern agriculture, but the key point is that the agriculture of the developed world, supported by massive government subsidises and dominated by a small number of corporations, comes at the expense of the more traditional, small-scale and subsistence farming that has historically characterised most of the world.[72]

This domination can be summed up by Cargill Inc. Founded in 1865 and based in Minnesota, Cargill is now one of the world's largest private corporations, with adjusted operating earnings of $3.2 billion in 2018. It employs 155,000 people in 70 countries, trading everything from cotton to animal feed, meat, cocoa and salt. The company says that "Cargill Beef is one of North America's largest beef processors, harvesting more than eight million cattle and producing nearly eight billion pounds of boxed beef and by-products each year". The company owns its own fleet of over 500 ships to help distribute its products, including 120 "capesize" vessels, the largest dry goods ships in service.[73]

Corporations like Cargill have enormous influence in the world food system. In 2005 four companies controlled processing of 80 percent of US beef, three of them, together with another fourth company, controlled 60 percent of US pork, and 50 percent of chicken production comes from another four companies.

Silvia Ribeiro and Hope Shand explain the negative role of big business in agriculture:

Corporate concentration in agriculture has allowed a handful of powerful corporations to seize the agricultural research agenda, influence national and international trade and agricultural policy and engineer the acceptance of new technologies as the "science-based"

72. I've explored this in detail in chapter 10 of my book, *Land and Labour: Marxism, Ecology and Human History* (Bookmarks, 2014).

73. All information on Cargill Inc from *www.cargill.com* (accessed February 2019).

solution to maximising food production. Although frequently promoted in the name of addressing the needs of the world's poor and hungry, the benefits of these technologies typically [accrue] to those who develop and control them.[74]

Because they are driven by maximisation of profits, companies like Cargill put their profits before the interests of the environment or people. Cargill, for instance, has been the focus of a campaign against destructive production of palm oil, which, according to the Rainforest Action Network, meant the company had a "role in orangutan extinction, rainforest destruction, child labour and human rights abuses".[75] Palm oil is widely used in food production, but increasingly is used as an ingredient in biofuels. Biofuels are promoted as an alternative to fossil fuels, but there are significant environmental problems associated with them and question marks over their ability to reduce emissions compared to existing fossil fuels.

But while acknowledging the dangers to food security and the environment, Cargill is concerned that its ability to make profits from the biofuel industry is not hampered by regulation:

Cargill believes biofuels can play an important role in meeting global energy and environmental needs, bringing capital investment to agriculture, and boosting economic development in farm communities. At the same time, we believe that the growth and development of the biofuels industry must be supported by verifiable environmental benefits — and that the production of biofuels from food crops should be balanced against the need to provide food for a growing global population, as well as the need to protect natural resources for future generations. We support government and

74. Quoted in Walden Bello, *The Food Wars* (Verso, 2009), pp110-111.

75. Rainforest Action Network (RAN), "Pressure is Working, Cargill is on the Move", 29 July 2014, *www.ran.org/pressure_is_working_cargill_is_on_the_move*

stakeholder efforts to achieve that balance. In terms of biofuels trade, Cargill favors market-driven policies that encourage gradual change, reliability and stability — rather than policies which impose artificial controls such as mandates, subsidies, export taxes, tariffs and other non-tariff barriers.[76]

Despite serious questions over their environmental credentials, biofuels are big business. In the run up to the passing of the 2014 Farm Act in the United States, major energy companies lobbied to ensure that subsidies for the fuel were protected. The amounts spent on lobbying can be astronomical. A report by the US Taxpayers for Common Sense, "Political Footprint of the Corn Ethanol Lobby", says that between 2007 and 2013 Cargill spent nearly $10 million on lobbying. Another major international food corporation, Archer Daniels Midland (ADM), spent nearly $11 million and the American Farm Bureau and State Organisations $38 million.[77]

The biofuel industry has a significant impact on food security and the environment. Yet the potential profits mean that corporations are prepared to fight to ensure they can continue to grow the crops. Paul McMahon explains the problem:

US biofuels policies have been strongly criticised for driving up the price of food, while delivering few environmental benefits...[these] policies have nothing to do with the environment, nor with feeding the poor. To a minor extent they are driven by a desire for energy security... But the primary objective of the biofuels policy is to provide financial support to American farmers. It is the latest in the long line of attempts to find uses for the country's grain surpluses.[78]

76. Quoted from *www.cargill.com/news/biofuels* (accessed February 2019).
77. See *www.taxpayer.net/library/article/updated-political-footprint-of-the-corn-ethanol-lobby*
78. McMahon, *Feeding Frenzy*, as above, p58.

There is a close link between the interests of agribusiness and those of national governments. The 2008 food crisis demonstrated that many countries were ill-prepared for price rises. In response a number of countries have begun to protect their interests by securing food elsewhere. Sometimes this has meant countries or corporations purchasing land for agriculture (or biofuels) in Africa and South America. These "land-grabs" have become shorthand for the way that peasant producers, local farming practices and the rights of indigenous peoples are brushed aside in the search for food security and profits.

Corporations often use the question of food security to justify their actions. In 2009, for instance, the Japanese trading house Mitsui was looking for "agricultural investments" in Central America, Asia and Eastern Europe. It offered "inputs and machinery to farmers in exchange for the right to buy harvests", explaining that this was "not only good business; it would also satisfy the Japanese government's desire to strengthen national food security".[79]

It was through meetings of the G8 and G20 that the major countries tried to shape a response to the 2008 food crisis. While globally the International Monetary Fund (IMF) and World Bank, as well as the World Trade Organisation, have shaped a neoliberal approach towards the development of the world economy, in terms of food and agriculture there are three key United Nations organisations. These are the International Fund for Agricultural Development, the World Food Programme (designed to manage food assistance to areas struck by drought, etc) and the Food and Agricultural Organisation (FAO). Finally, the Consultative Group in International Agricultural Research (CGIAR) is a body linked to the World Bank that tries to "extend the legacy of the original green revolution of the 1960s and 1970s by using science to develop improved seeds and more productive and sustainable farming...in the developing world".[80]

79. McMahon, *Feeding Frenzy,* as above, p171.
80. Paarlberg, *Food Politics,* as above, pp210-211.

All these bodies serve to ensure that neoliberal policies continue to sink deeper into world food and agriculture. What this means in practice can be seen from the World Bank and IMF structural adjustment programmes (SAPs) of the 1980s and 1990s. These systematically reduced the role of the state in agriculture in the developing world and promoted the production of food for trade. As US agriculture secretary John Block explained in 1986, "the idea that developing countries should feed themselves is an anachronism from a bygone era. They could better ensure their food security by relying on US agricultural products, which are available in most cases at a lower cost".[81]

But even the World Bank had to admit that the result of the SAPs was a disaster for agriculture. In its 2008 World Development Report it acknowledged:

> Structural adjustment in the 1980s dismantled the elaborate system of public agencies that provided farmers with access to land, credit, insurance, inputs and cooperative organisations. The expectation was that removing the state would free the market for private actors to take over these functions... Incomplete markets and institutional gaps impose huge costs in forgone growth and welfare losses for smallholders, threatening their competitiveness and, in many cases, their survival.[82]

World Bank policies decimated African smallholder and peasant farming in the interests of corporate agribusiness. The consequences were appalling, with the rural population displaced, driven into unemployment or underemployment or forced to seek work in the cities. As neoliberal policies enforce a switch to larger-scale farming at the expense of local, small-scale agriculture, they also have negative consequences

81. Quoted in Bello, *The Food Wars*, as above, p76.
82. Quoted in Bello, as above, p81.

for the environment. Even the UK government admitted in 2011 that:

> Many systems of food production are unsustainable. Without change, the global food system will continue to degrade the environment and compromise the world's capacity to produce food in the future, as well as contributing to climate change and the destruction of biodiversity... Nothing less is required than a redesign of the whole food system to bring sustainability to the fore.[83]

Is meat eating the problem?

Reducing emissions from agriculture will not be tackled by individuals switching to a non-meat based diet. The environmental damage from farming is a result of the nature of the industry under capitalism, with production determined by the need to make profits. Arguing for a switch to a meat-free diet is a dangerous strategy for the environmental movement because it places the blame on individuals as consumers, not the system as a whole.

As one scientist commented while reviewing *Cowspiracy*:

> Movies like *Cowspiracy* aren't believable, not only because of how they twist the science, but also because of what they ask us to believe: that the fossil fuel industry...aren't the main cause of global warming; that the transition to clean energy isn't what matters most for our future and our grandchildren's; and that thousands of scientists have covered up the truth about the most important environmental issue of our time.[84]

The much derided "Western diet" that we are told is

83. Quoted in McMahon, *Feeding Frenzy*, as above, p69.

84. Doug Boucher, "There's a Vast Cowspiracy about Climate Change", Union of Concerned Scientists, 2016, http://blog.ucsusa.org/doug-boucher/cowspiracy-movie-review

unhealthy and destructive for the environment is not a consequence of consumer choice, but is a result of corporate interests.
Beef production on the US grasslands became closely associated
with the production of grain. So profitable was the growing of
grain for cattle feed, that from the late 1950s there was a drive
to encourage more beef consumption. As Elaine Graham-Leigh
has pointed out: "beef eating was so profitable that it was in
companies' interests to ensure that US consumption remained
high. Consumers may have felt they were making a free choice
to eat hamburgers, but there was in fact a concerted effort to
encourage them to do so".[85]

The choices that individuals make about food are very
personal, but they are also shaped by the world that they live in.
Processed food might be worse for the environment and your
health, but for the parent returning home from a long shift it's
a quick way to feed their children. Time is one factor, but so is
the cost of food with junk food being cheaper per calorie than
other options.[86]

This is not to say we should not criticise the meat industry
for its impact on the environment or our health. Questions of
obesity and malnutrition are questions of class, as much as
those of production. Elaine Graham-Leigh writes:

An argument which says that the production of large
amounts of nutrient-poor, energy-dense food in the
West is problematic for food consumption worldwide
and for the climate (and has a tendency to make some
individuals become fatter than they would otherwise
be) is a world away from one which says that regardless
of the interests vested in that pattern of food production and consumption, the responsibility lies only with
those people who become fat because of it.[87]

85. Graham-Leigh, *A Diet of Austerity,* as above, p56.
86. As above, p172.
87. As above, p17.

The struggle for a sustainable agriculture will simultaneously be a struggle for healthier diets, with a corresponding decrease in meat consumption for some, but an increase for others. Doing this sustainably will mean challenging the priorities of a food system which, because it is driven by profit not the need to feed people, can waste a third of food produced for human consumption, equivalent to more than half the world's annual cereal crops.[88] It means changing the energy intensive factory farming that currently dominates in the developed world which means that a tonne of maize grown in the US uses 160 litres of oil compared to less than 5 litres in Mexico.[89] It will also require an end to factory farming and the over-production of meat, which uses vast areas of land to grow livestock food, with an enormous impact on the environment, and promotes an unhealthy diet. Currently the cereals used to feed factory farmed animals could feed 3 billion people.[90]

Production under capitalism is not determined by need, or simply by consumer demand, but what is profitable; and the food industry is particularly adept at creating demand for its products. Fighting for sustainability in food and agriculture will not come by lecturing individuals demanding they stop buying meat products, but through a root and branch transformation of the food system itself.

The alternative

As we have seen, greenhouse gas emissions from agriculture could be significantly reduced even within the existing system. But whether or not farmers and agribusiness will find it worthwhile to invest in technology or change established practices to reduce environmental impacts will depend on incentives and their ability to maintain profits. As the FAO points out in regard to livestock farming, though it applies equally to other

88. See the FAO's "Key Facts on Food Loss and Waste you Should Know!", www.fao.org/save-food/resources/keyfindings/en/
89. Magdoff and Tokar, Agriculture and Food in Crisis, as above, p65.
90. Lymbery, Farmageddon, as above, p253.

sectors of agriculture: "In the absence of financial incentives (eg mitigation subsidies) or regulations to limit emissions, most producers are unlikely to invest in mitigation practices unless they increase profits or provide other production benefits such as risk reduction".[91]

Creating a truly sustainable agriculture capable of feeding a growing world population through the 21st century will mean challenging the priorities of the world food system, the interests of agricultural big business and international bodies such as the World Bank. This will require political and economic struggles by the world's working class and peasantry.

One solution offered by some commentators is "biodiverse ecological farming". This means rejecting industrialised agriculture and encouraging small-scale farming. One of the leading proponents of this approach, Vandana Shiva, notes that "under globalisation, the farmer is losing her/his social, cultural and economic identity as a producer. A farmer is now a 'consumer' of costly seeds and costly chemicals sold by powerful global corporations through powerful landlords and moneylenders locally".[92]

Agriculture, as practised by millions of smallholders and peasant farmers in the developing world, can be more sustainable, and more efficient at feeding populations healthily and well. However, a longer-term vision for sustainable farming cannot simply be a return to smallholding farming on a global scale. This is not to dismiss peasant agriculture. Small farms are usually portrayed as being unproductive, but the opposite is true and they tend to have other benefits — a lower impact on the environment, lower use of fossil fuels, the promotion and protection of biodiversity, and greater resilience to storms and hurricanes.[93] Because smallholders avoid monoculture farming, they also produce more food per area than highly focused

91. Gerber and others, "Tackling Climate Change Through Livestock", as above, p60.

92. Quoted in Bello, *The Food Wars*, as above, pp35-36.

93. Miguel A Altieri, "Agroecology, Small Farms and Food Sovereignty", *Monthly Review*, volume 61, issue 3, 2009, *www.monthlyreview.org/2009/07/01/agroecology-small-farms-and-food-sovereignty/*

industrialised farming. However, this relies on the back-breaking work of peasant families. The working population in agriculture is about 1.3 billion people worldwide. A third of these rely on animal power and a further third use only manual tools. Thus some 400 million peasants feed a further 1 billion using only manual tools, without fertiliser, tractors, pesticides or livestock feed. This requires long hours of hard manual labour.[94]

As the German Marxist Karl Kautsky noted in his classic 1889 study The Agrarian Question, it would take "a very obdurate admirer of small-scale land ownership to see the advantages derived from forcing small cultivators down to the level of beasts of burden, into a life occupied by nothing other than work — apart from time set aside for sleeping and eating".[95]

There are, however, growing social movements among small and peasant farmers for greater control of land and their livelihoods. One recent comparative study of social movements in South and Central America concludes:

> For thousands of landless people in Brazil and for thousands of indigenous peasants in Chiapas, joining the MST [The Brazilian Landless Movement] or the EZLN [the Mexican Zapatista Army of National Liberation] is a profoundly life-changing experience. Casting their lot with the MST or the EZLN is a political experience that has allowed them to gain or protect their access to land and provide for their families. It is an experience that politicises them and generates a sense of individual and collective agency that throughout their lives they often felt they did not have.[96]

But these social movements are not enough to transform

94. Marcel Mazoyer and Laurence Roudart, *A History of World Agriculture: From the Neolithic Age to the Current Crisis* (Monthly Review Press, 2006), p13.

95. Karl Kautsky, *The Agrarian Question, volume 1* (Zwan Publications, 1988), p111.

96. Leandro Vergara-Camus, *Land and Freedom: The MST, the Zapatistas and Peasant Alternatives to Neoliberalism* (Zed Books, 2014), p301.

the global food system and its domination by big agribusiness. Doing this will require the development of wider alliances that can directly challenge the capitalist agriculture system.

As Miguel A Altieri has pointed out:

> Rural social movements understand that dismantling the industrial agri-food complex and restoring local food systems must be accompanied by the construction of agro-ecological alternatives that suit the needs of small-scale producers and the low-income non-farming population, and that oppose corporate control over production and consumption... Moving toward a more socially just, economically viable, and environmentally sound agriculture will be the result of the coordinated action of emerging social movements in the rural sector in alliance with civil society organisations that are committed to supporting the goals of these farmers' movements.[97]

Small farmers are locked into a wider global network of commodities, with capital tending to invest upstream and downstream in the supply of pesticides, genetically modified crops and equipment or in the distribution of food. In fact, the persistence of small-scale farmers and the peasantry is itself in part a result of the needs of a larger agricultural capitalism which needs their labour at specific times of the year, but requires them to subsist on their own smallholdings in between.[98] For millions of peasants there is no way out of this trap without fundamental changes to the economic system. In the developed world most farmers are no longer the smallholding producers they are traditionally seen as, but contractors servicing the

97. Altieri, "Agroecology, Small Farms and Food Sovereignty", as above, p112.

98. Julio Boltvinik, "Poverty and the Persistence of the Peasantry", background paper, *Poverty and Peasant Persistence in the Contemporary World* seminar, March 2012, *www.crop.org/viewfile.aspx?id=261*

bigger corporations and dependent on the whims of the super-markets.[99] Breaking this cycle of poverty and hard labour means transforming agriculture, not romanticising a particular form of peasant agriculture.

Conclusion

In his studies of the works of the German chemist Justus von Liebig, Karl Marx developed a critique of the unsustainable nature of agriculture under capitalism, closely linked to his concept of the metabolic rift. Marx argued that there could be a rational agriculture, but it would mean the transformation of production and land ownership. Under capitalism, "instead of a conscious and rational treatment of the land as permanent communal property, as the inalienable condition for the exist-ence and reproduction of the chain of human generations, we have the exploitation and the squandering of the powers of the earth".[100]

In 1964 Tony Cliff wrote a self-described "revisionist" account: "Marxism and the Collectivisation of Agriculture". Cliff argued that the immediate impact of a socialist revolution would probably be to "give the private farm a new lease of life under the socialist regime". But the transformation of produc-tion would gradually undermine this:

> The socialist regime, by raising living standards all round, assuring security of employment, and compre-hensive pensions for old age and sickness, will deflate the value of economic "independence" represented in the private ownership of the farm... Thus the organisa-tion of agriculture in co-operative farms is bound to be

99. Thanks to Ian Rappel for this point.

100. Marx, *Capital, vol 3*, as above, pp948-949. It should be noted that here Marx criticises both "small-scale" and "large-scale" agriculture for this failing, but argues that they fail for different reasons. Small-scale farming is at fault because of "a lack of the resources and science needed to apply the social productive powers of labour", but in the case of large-scale agriculture it is because of the "exploitation of such means for the most rapid enrichment of farmer and proprietor".

an extremely slow process, impeded by some factors that are brought into play by the new socialist regime, not gaining much stimulation from the assumed decline of small farming under the technical superiority of the large ones. The process of the transition of agriculture from individual to collectivist methods will thus be the result of the abundance of wealth and culture in highly developed societies. Individual farming will not be over-thrown, but sublimated.[101]

It is only agriculture like this, rooted in the collective ownership of the land and the means of production, that will be able to produce enough healthy food to feed the world in a sustainable way in the long term.

***

---

101. Tony Cliff, "Marxism and the Collectivisation of Agriculture", *International Socialism* 19, first series, winter 1964-5, *www.marxists.org/archive/cliff/works/1964/xx/*

Chapter 7
Capitalism and the Biodiversity Crisis
Sarah Ensor

Into the Sixth Extinction?

We are living through the highest rates of species extinction since the dinosaurs were killed 65 million years ago. The WWF's *Living Blue Planet Report* in 2015[1] found that marine vertebrate populations including cod, haddock, salmon and tuna had dropped by 49 percent in just over 40 years. A quarter of shark, ray and skate species are now threatened by extinction from overfishing and environmental degradation.

Farmland birds in France have declined by around 30 percent since the 1980s while Britain has lost 56 percent of species such as skylarks and partridges. Whales, turtles and seabirds die as they fill their stomachs with plastic waste mistaken for food. Coral reefs that form nurseries for 25 percent of the world's fish are threatened by acidification and warming water linked to climate change.

1. WWF, *Living Blue Planet Report*, September 2015, *https://www.worldwildlife.org/publications/living-blue-planet-report-2015*

Recent studies[2] show that insect populations have dropped by up to 98 percent in the Puerto Rican rainforest over the last 40 years, by up to 80 percent in Mexican forests and by 75 percent in Germany's nature reserves. These catastrophic levels of insect loss are linked to rising temperatures and pollution, but the biggest driver is the destruction of their habitats[3] exacerbated by the global use of glyphosate weedkillers and neonicotinoid insecticides. As the insects vanish, thousands of species of birds, lizards and mammals whose food relies on insects cannot breed successfully so they disappear.

The Catalogue of Life project[4] records 1.8 million species, of which roughly 200,000 species have been identified in the last five years. But we are driving species extinct before we have had time to describe them and understand their place in Charles Darwin's "tangled bank" of biodiversity[5] where many

2. Bradford C Lister and Andres Garcia, "Climate-driven declines in arthropod abundance restructure a rainforest food web", Proceedings of the National Academy of Sciences of the United States of America, September 2018 https://www.pnas.org/content/115/44/E10397; Caspar A Hallmann, Martin Sorg, Eelke Jongejans, Henk Siepel, Nick Hofland, Heinz Schwan, Werner Stenmans, Andreas Müller, Hubert Sumser, Thomas Hörren, Dave Goulson, Hans de Kroon, "More than 75 percent decline over 27 years in total flying insect biomass in protected areas", Plos One Journal, October 2017, https://journals.plos.org/plosone/article?id=10.1371/journal.pone.0185809

3. Michael Le Page, "Huge global extinction risk for insects could be worse than we thought", New Scientist, 11 February 2019, https://www.newscientist.com/article/2193494-huge-global-extinction-risk-for-insects-could-be-worse-than-we-thought/

4. See www.catalogueoflife.org

5. Charles Darwin, On the Origin of the Species, 1859. Later editions were edited to include reference to a "Creator" but the original final paragraph of the first edition reads: "It is interesting to contemplate an entangled bank, clothed with many plants of many kinds, with birds singing on the bushes, with various insects flitting about, and with worms crawling through the damp earth, and to reflect that these elaborately constructed forms, so different from each other, and dependent on each other in so complex a manner, have all been produced by laws acting around us. These laws, taken in the largest sense, being Growth with Reproduction; Inheritance which is almost implied by reproduction; Variability from the indirect and direct action of the external conditions of life, and from use and disuse; a Ratio of Increase so high as to lead to a Struggle for Life, and as a consequence to Natural Selection, entailing Divergence of Character and the Extinction of less-improved forms. Thus, from the war of nature, from famine and death, the most exalted object which we are capable of conceiving, namely, the production of the higher animals, directly follows. There is grandeur in this view of life, with its several powers, having been originally breathed into a few forms or into one; and that, whilst this planet has gone cycling on according to the fixed law of gravity, from so simple a beginning endless forms most beautiful and most wonderful have been, and are being, evolved."

organisms rely on each other to thrive and in turn support many other organisms in a complex web of co-dependency. This means that driving one species extinct or near extinct can have a cascade of unintended effects.

What is driving the biodiversity crisis and why does it matter?
The interactions between insects, worms, micro-organisms and plant matter form fertile soil, so as we destroy insects we destroy the very basis for our food chain. Glyphosate weed-killers and neonicotinoid insecticides were developed in the 1980s to replace the poisonous previous generation of pesticides including DDT, that were famously challenged in Rachel Carson's 1962 book, *Silent Spring*. Agrochemical industries, dominated by firms such as Monsanto, recently bought by pharmaceutical giant Bayer, grew up developing the glyphosate "Roundup" weedkillers — and from the mid-1990s genetically engineered crops designed to survive them called "Roundup Ready". Both governments and environmental organisations championed these chemicals as they destroyed pollinators, especially bees, wrecked ecosystems and drove hundreds of thousands of farmers on every continent into debt and suicide.

Industrial farming is all about inputs whether weedkillers, insecticides, artificial nitrate fertilisers poured onto exhausted arable land, or antibiotics and growth enhancers fed to livestock. This is not because farmers don't care about their animals and land, but because under capitalism each farm is a business that must maximise profit against its competitors, other farmers. Arable industrial farming has maximised profit by increasing the use of machinery and field size and has broken up ecosystems by turning grasslands into vast swathes of single crops and chopping down rainforests for soybeans and avocados.

Industrial meat production has developed the feed lot system where animals spend their whole lives penned indoors or in small outdoor areas, unable to behave like animals. The drive for profit demands that a cow is no longer a herd animal that needs sunshine, fresh water and space to roam for grasses and other plants that its complex biology turns into milk. It is reduced to a milk and calf machine worth so much profit for each square metre. Feed lots become highly profitable centres of pollution, disease, antibiotic resistance and animal misery. Much of the food for animals kept in this way in the European Union comes from soybeans grown in Brazil. Cattle pasture is ploughed up to grow soybeans, which leads to more deforestation as land is cleared for animal rearing.[6] Industrial agriculture causes further environmental damage as pesticides, fertilisers and animal waste run off farmland into streams and rivers, causing dead zones in estuaries and along coasts where algae blooms starve the water of oxygen, forcing species to move or die.

Industrial fishing treats the oceans with the same indifference to biodiversity, so species from Antarctic krill to Atlantic cod are commodified and valued for profit, not for their place in the ecosystem. But there are much larger threats to some species than fishing. The small, fatty Arctic or polar cod (Boreogadus saida) has evolved to thrive in waters around 0°C by producing "antifreeze" glycoprotein to reduce the freezing temperatures of its own body fluids. These fish mature in just two to three years and lay their eggs under sea ice for protection. As high energy food they support hundreds of species including humans, narwhals, seabirds, seals, walruses and, indirectly, polar bears. They are also turned into fishmeal. But none of this is a threat to their existence. As global warming causes sea ice to disappear the Arctic cod's eggs and larvae will float freely in the open and be easy prey for seabirds, as well as the Atlantic cod moving north to find cooler water. If the eggs come into contact with even small amounts of oil pollution the larvae are born malformed and are unable to grow and breed.

The loss of sea ice should be a loud warning about impending disaster, but energy corporations see an opportunity for further oil exploration as the ice disappears, which

6. Philip Lymbery, "The Great Disappearing Act", in Joyce D'Silva and Carol McKenna, *Farming Food and Nature* (Earthscan, 2015), p18.

can only exacerbate climate change and species loss. A recent report from the Arctic Monitoring and Assessment Programme[7] shows that if climate change isn't challenged effectively then many species in the Arctic will die out even if we stopped hunting them immediately.

Capitalism is anti-ecological

So why can't we just stop cutting down the rainforests to grow palm trees, avocados or soya? Why don't we just stop overfishing and tackle climate change? The mainstream answers we get to these expressions of exasperation include selfish human nature, irresponsible corporations, meat eaters and, of course, too many people. But the reality is that we have a systemic problem because what links biodiversity crisis to industrial meat production, deforestation, overfishing, rising temperatures and extreme weather events is capitalism's drive for profit.

Frederick Engels, Karl Marx's great collaborator, made the point in 1876 that capitalists are not interested in consequences. He wrote:

As individual capitalists are engaged in production and exchange for the sake of immediate profit, only the nearest, most immediate results must be taken into account. As long as the individual manufacturer or merchant sells a manufactured or purchased commodity with the usual coveted profit, he is satisfied and does not concern himself with what afterwards becomes of the commodity and its purchasers... What cared the Spanish planters in Cuba, who burned down forests on the slopes of the mountains and obtained from the ashes sufficient fertiliser for one generation of highly profitable coffee trees? What cared they that the heavy tropical rainfall afterwards washed away the

7. Arctic Monitoring and Assessment Programme, "AMAP Assessment 2018: Arctic Ocean Acidification". www.amap.no/documents/doc/AMAP-Assessment-2018-Arctic-Ocean-Acidification/1659

unprotected upper stratum of the soil, leaving behind only bare rock?[8]

Few capitalists set out to destroy biodiversity but it is an inevitable by-product of the processes that exalt the accumulation of profit above all other considerations. The problem is not necessarily industrial development because ecosystems are endlessly inventive and dynamic. In Britain goldfinches have become garden birds in the last few decades and perhaps 150,000 red foxes now live in towns and cities[9] eating rats and food waste or being fed by their human neighbours. But if industrial scale destruction of biodiversity combined with climate change is not challenged, large areas of Earth will become uninhabitable as the ecological networks that we rely on collapse.

The capitalist solutions to problems created by capitalism are completely inadequate and as we saw with glyphosate and neonicotinoids, usually make the problem worse because they refuse to challenge capitalism's drive for profit. As Ian Rappel shows elsewhere in this book, you cannot solve crises created by capitalism by applying the theory and practice of capitalism to ecosystems and biodiversity as "natural capital" and "environmental services". Nor does the solution lie in ideas of handing half the earth to nature, as if humans were not inextricably part of the natural world; as if it were not also our survival and our wellbeing at stake.

Over the last few years we have seen "rewilding" projects designed to boost biodiversity by reintroducing lynx, beavers, golden eagles or wolves but these will not solve a problem that lies in the system's relationship to soil, land use, the oceans and how we produce food.

---

8. Frederick Engels, *The Part Played by Labour in the Transition from Ape to Man,* 1883, *https://www.marxists.org/archive/marx/works/1883/don/ch09.htm*

9. Aisling Irwin, "There are five times more urban foxes in England than we thought", *New Scientist,* 4 January 2017, *www.newscientist.com/article/2116583-there-are-five-times-more-urban-foxes-in-england-than-we-thought/*

Socialism and biodiversity conservation

The real solutions to our climate and biodiversity crises lie in transforming our relationship to the natural world in a broader challenge to capitalism's drive for profit. To achieve this we must replace capitalism with a socialist system. Under socialism, rewilding and other forms of biodiversity conservation are more likely to succeed because a democratic and rational approach towards food production and our "use" of nature and natural resources will mean that we won't force other life forms to compete with capital and its profit motive. This is how we could develop humanity's ecological understanding and our collective aesthetic and moral valuation of nature in its many and various wonderful forms. This is how we could shape a convivial, sustainable Anthropocene.

***

Chapter 8
Why Capitalism Loves Plastic
Amy Leather

In 2017 many people were shocked by images on the BBC TV
programme Blue Planet of a sperm whale with a stomach full
of plastic waste, albatrosses feeding their young plastic and
turtles trapped in plastic bags.[1]

A report prepared in 2016 for the billionaires attending
the annual World Economic Forum in Davos, Switzerland, estimates that there are more than 150 million tonnes of plastics in
the oceans already, with another 8 million tonnes being added
each year. That's five trillion pieces of plastic in the ocean and
counting. If we carry on at this rate, by 2050 plastics in the
ocean will outweigh all the fish.

But there is a contradiction. Plastic is causing great harm
to the environment, and yet it is a fantastic material that has
allowed for advances in medicine, hygiene, food preservation, water transportation and much more. Our starting point
should be that plastic does not exist in isolation, separate from
the world in which it is produced.

In many ways the story of plastics gets to the heart of
what's wrong with capitalism. It is a by-product of the fossil fuel

1. This is an updated version of an article that appeared on the *Climate and Capitalism* web
journal in November 2018.

industry — 99 percent of all plastics are produced from chemicals sourced from oil and gas. Its production was driven by the relentless drive for profit at the heart of the system. War further fuelled its development, while state investment helped increase production, and from the outset vested interests have encouraged us to use more plastic.

Even today, when millions of people would like to cut down our plastic use, production of new virgin plastic is actually increasing. Far from being driven by "consumer demand" — and therefore the fault of individual consumers — plastic production is locked into the fossil fuel-based economy of modern industrial capitalism. That is where we must look for the root of the climate crisis.

Plastic production began in the mid-19th century, when celluloid, derived from the natural cellulose polymer in plants, was developed as a substitute for ivory. The first truly synthetic plastic was Bakelite, introduced in 1907 as a substitute for shellac. It paved the way for mass production, as scientists were no longer trying to emulate nature but instead seeking to "rearrange nature in new and imaginative ways". The 1920s and 1930s saw an outpouring of new materials from labs around the world.

Meanwhile, the many uses of oil were being discovered. As Ian Angus shows in his book *Facing the Anthropocene*, while oil companies were busy building markets for petroleum as fuel, paving the way for the mass production of cars, the chemical industry was developing entirely new materials made from the by-products of oil refining.

Legend has it, according to Susan Freinkel's book *Plastic: A Love Story,* that John D Rockefeller was looking out over one of his oil refineries when he noticed flames flaring from some smokestacks. When he asked what was burning, he was told that the company was burning off ethylene gas, a by-product of the refining process. "I don't believe in wasting anything," Rockefeller supposedly snapped, "figure out something to do with it."

True or not, that story sums up the origins of the modern

petrochemical industry — the principle that every hydrocarbon taken from the ground can be used to make a profit.

The "something" that could be produced from burning ethylene was polyethylene, discovered in 1933. It was so unlike any other known polymer that no one could envisage a use for it. But inexpensive, durable and pliable polyethylene became the most commonly used polymer.

It made sense to co-locate fossil fuel and plastic production and so in the early 20th century, petroleum and chemical companies began to develop alliances and form vertically integrated companies. Today the largest players — DowDuPont, ExxonMobil, Shell, Chevron, BP and Sinopec — have their roots in the early decades of the 20th century and are integrated companies that produce both fossil fuels and plastics.

Plastic production took off in the 1930s, but it was the Second World War that transformed production and paved the way for the widespread use of plastics in everyday life in the post-war period. War allowed plastic to showcase its versatility. The major plastics we know today — polyethylene, nylon, acrylic, polystyrene — were put to use during the war. The US government spent over $3 billion on building or expanding petrochemical plants during the war, quadrupling plastic production by 1945.

When hostilities ended, US oil and chemical companies were able to buy these factories at bargain basement prices. As early as 1943 DuPont had devoted a whole division to prepare prototypes of housewares that could be made of the plastics which at that point were being commandeered for the war, and such products became the basis of the post-war plastic explosion.

The buoyant and insulating polystyrene, used by the US Coast Guard for life rafts, was now used for picnic cups and coolers. Polyethylene's extraordinary capacity to insulate at high frequencies was side lined for a new career bagging sandwiches and dry cleaning. As one early plastics executive recalled, by the war's end it was obvious that "virtually nothing was made from plastic and anything could be". It was also clear that by expanding products made of plastic vast profits could be made.

And so plastics entered our homes, our cars, our clothes, our playthings, our workplaces, even our bodies.

In discussions about plastic use it is common to blame mass consumerism and a throwaway culture for the environmental problem of plastic. However, rather than being demand led, the throwaway culture was created and driven by the corporations who profit from it.

The amazing materials created from the waste products of the oil and gas industry had to first be turned into new products and then a demand created for that new use. But the industry faced a big problem. Plastic is characterised by its strength and durability. A plastic product can last a long time, negating the need to buy another. So the industry had to come up with new ways to make us want and need more plastic.

It was this drive for profit that led to single-use plastic and thus created the era of disposability. As a speaker at a 1956 conference told an audience of plastics manufacturers, "Your future is in the garbage wagon."

Disposable products were initially a hard sell to a generation that had come through the Depression and war-time, when a "make do and mend" mantra meant nothing was wasted. People initially kept the new plastic goods rather than throwing them away after one use, for example saving the plastic cups from vending machines to reuse.

Massive media campaigns were launched to change attitudes, epitomised by an article in *Life* magazine that celebrated what it dubbed "Throwaway Living." It was illustrated with a photo of a young couple and child with their arms raised in exultation amid a downpour of disposable items — plates, cutlery, bags, ashtrays, dog dishes, pails, BBQ grills and more. It calculated that cleaning all the items would take 40 hours but now "no housewife need bother."

Similarly, plastic bags, the epitome of single-use plastic, were unpopular when they were first introduced in the mid-1970s — shoppers did not like the fact that the cashier had to lick their fingers to get them free. But in the end the big stores were won over by economics. Paper bags cost three to four times as much, and once one or two big chains introduced them, all switched to plastic.

Products were redesigned to be used only once, from lighters to pens, razors to straws. Today half of all plastics produced go into single-use applications, and at the heart of this is packaging, which accounts for 26 percent of all production.

Perhaps nothing sums up the irrationality of capitalism more than this — materials that can last practically forever are used to make products designed to be thrown away.

And so this brings us to where we are today — swimming in plastic. According to a recent study published in Science Advances, 8.3 billion tonnes of the stuff has been produced since the early 20th century. And production keeps on rising, with approximately 400 million tonnes of plastic being produced globally each year.

Worldwide, people use somewhere between 500 billion and 1 trillion plastic bags a year — more than a million a minute. So it is not surprising that plastic bags have become a primary target in our desire to cut down on single-use plastic.

However, *New Scientist* recently calculated a cotton tote bag must be used 131 times before its environmental cost falls below that of a disposable plastic bag, mostly because of the impact of growing cotton. Similarly, purely in energy terms, because a steel water bottle takes so much energy to make, it needs to be used 500 times compared to a disposable bottle.

Another way to limit the amount of plastic ending up in our oceans is to recycle more of it. Just 14 percent of all plastic across the world is collected for recycling, and of that only one-third — 5 percent of all production — is actually recycled. The rest is either burned, sent to landfill or enters the environment as pollution.

In theory all plastic could be recycled, but there are many barriers in practice. The lack of uniform recycling facilities is a problem. The many different types of plastic need to be sorted and recycled separately. While many facilities still sort by hand and cannot process most plastic, a state of the art waste and recycling centre in Southwark, south London, shines light onto discarded plastic travelling down a conveyor belt; the reflection indicates the type of plastic and air jets push each type into a different stream. The plant can even recycle plastic bags and black plastic food trays, which are the hardest to recycle.

However, even the most sophisticated processing centres still face the problem of mixed plastics in one product, favoured by manufacturers. And in a capitalist economy, no recycling process is viable unless there is a market for the recycled product. Many manufacturers demand clear plastic packaging which is very difficult to produce from recycled.

Two-thirds of Britain's plastic waste is sent abroad for recycling. For many years China was at the centre of the global recycling trade. However, its announcement in 2017 that it will no longer take "foreign rubbish" has meant traders have had to look for other countries to take their recycling waste. The industry is undergoing unprecedented disruption with allegations of smuggling, corruption and pollution. Recent exposés have shown that much of our exported plastic waste is just burnt or dumped in landfill sites from Turkey to Malaysia. Many countries that originally thought they would fill the space left by China have found they cannot cope with the amount of rubbish and have frozen imports of plastic and other waste. In America plastic, paper and glass set aside for recycling has been stuffed into landfills or simply burned in vast volumes leading to toxic pollution.

All this doesn't stop manufacturers cynically trying to exploit people's concerns over plastic waste. Many realised early on that claiming their product was recyclable would help sales, even if the facilities to recycle it did not exist. In most cases, big business finds it cheaper to produce new plastic than to recycle. Even companies such as Shell and Mobil that announced in January 2019 they were collaborating alongside other firms to try and tackle plastic pollution by reducing plastic production and improving recycling are in fact at the heart of a global boom in plastic production.

And this is the crux of the issue — even if we can increase recycling rates, which of course we should fight for, it won't be effective unless recycled plastics replace newly manufactured plastic in production. In reality, the giant multinationals of the fossil fuel and petro-chemical industries are right now increasing plastic production and planning for more.

Fracking and the so-called shale revolution in the US have helped fuel the plastic industry in recent years. US fracked natural gas is rich in ethane, needed to create ethylene, a primary feedstock for plastic. Fracking has led to a glut of cheap ethane that is even profitable for export. For example, fracked gas first arrived in 2016 at the Grangemouth works in Scotland, owned by Ineos, amid much furore from anti-fracking campaigners. The fact that this fracked gas would be used to make more plastic was rather overlooked at the time.

According to *Plastic News* in 2013 "shale based natural gas represents a once in a generation opportunity for the North American plastics market." At the time of writing there are a number of new plastics plants under construction. Shell is building a multibillion dollar plant in Pennsylvania which will use shale gas to produce 1.6 million metric tonnes of polyethylene — the world's most common plastic — every year. It is worth noting that Shell received $1.65 billion in tax credits from the state of Pennsylvania to help finance the plant. Mobil is building a new polyethylene production line at its plant in Texas to increase plastic production to more than 2.5 tonnes, making it one of the largest plastic production units in the world. Meanwhile Saudi Arabia's state oil company Saudi Aramco and the country's chemical giant SABIC are building one of the world's largest oil-to-petrochemicals factories.

The hypocrisy of these companies is breathtaking. Shell and Mobil are both founding companies behind a self-styled alliance to end plastic waste alongside other giant petro-chemical companies.

As capitalism fails to break from its reliance on oil and gas, and instead expands upon the fossil fuel infrastructure already created, it continues to be logical — and highly profitable — to use the waste products to make more and more plastic.

So what do we do? Firstly, rather than take a moralistic approach to consumers, we need to push the blame upwards, to direct our anger at the producers of plastic and the oil and gas companies and at the governments that let them frack. They must be made responsible for what happens to waste plastic.

Public outcry has already won some changes. The European Union is preparing a ban on single-use plastics including cutlery, straws and plates. The UK government is set to introduce a Plastics Pact, under which the companies responsible for 80 percent of plastic used in the UK pledge to make all plastic packaging to be recyclable, reusable and compostable, and to eliminate all single-use plastic packaging by 2025. This is a start, although limited by being voluntary rather than binding.

We should demand and fight for better recycling facilities, in our communities and workplaces. We should strive to collectivise our response to plastic production, and point the finger of blame upwards at the massive oil, gas and petrochemical companies that are pumping it out rather than the moral failure of individuals in society.

But none of this goes far enough. To prevent catastrophic climate change we need to leave fossil fuels in the ground. To stop our oceans and natural world being clogged up with plastic we need to massively reduce plastic production.

The logic of capitalism — the pursuit of profit — dictates the opposite. It is quite possible to imagine a world with less or even no plastic — after all it has only come into widespread use since the 1950s! — but it would be anathema for capitalists to abandon their sunken investments in the fossil fuel infrastructure or to give up producing something so profitable.

So we will have to force them to act. Anti-fracking campaigns have been immensely important in Britain in stopping, or at least slowing down the spread of the fossil fuel landscape.

But we also have to look at where power lies in society to take on these mammoth corporations. When Ineos truck drivers walked out on strike in 2013, it threatened to cut off oil to half of Scotland, hitting Ineos's profits hard.

When French energy workers went on strike against a new work law they blockaded fuel depots leading to a petrol shortage, while electricity production dropped and had to be imported.

These examples give a glimpse of the potential power of workers. They show a collective power that not only stops production and hits profits but could also transform society totally.

Plastic is an amazing material that has been distorted by capitalism. In a socialist society where people have real democratic control over resources and production processes there would need to be a discussion about how we use plastic, if at all. If we broke from fossil fuels and left oil and gas in the ground, it would bring to an end the production of nearly all the plastic we use today. In that situation we might want to consider developing plant-based plastics to replace synthetic ones, alongside other alternatives. Crucially we would be able to make rational decisions about how such strong and durable substances should be used. All of this would have to be taken in the wider environmental context of carbon emissions, energy use and waste.

But this will require fundamental change. We must fight now to prevent further expansion of the fossil fuel landscape and to stop more plastic entering our environment. But we must link it to wider demands and a movement that can challenge all the priorities of capitalism.

***

Chapter 9
Canada's Tar Sands, Indigenous Sovereignty and a Just Transition for Workers

Carolyn Egan and Michelle Robidoux

"Imagine you have a decent life, working hard, raising your family with a home on the edge of a town and the forest. Then one day, a forest fire breaks out and threatens to engulf your home. You grab everything you can in your two arms and flee with your family. The fire continues to follow, until as you run you come to a river. You only have two choices: to perish or to discard everything you own and swim across. Or, if you had started earlier, you could have built a bridge."

These words were spoken by Ken Smith, a heavy equipment operator in Fort McMurray, Alberta, at the Paris climate summit in 2015.[1] Smith, president of his union local, worked in the tar sands, a huge area in western Canada where tens of thousands are employed by multinational oil companies extracting bitumen from the ground. He had worked for decades as a

1. *www.nationalobserver.com/2015/12/08/news/cop21-oil-sands-worker-urges-smooth-transition-fossil-fuels*

miner in New Brunswick, his home province. When the mine shut down, he moved west for a job that would put food on the table and a roof over his family's head. His is the story of many tar sands workers who feel they have no choice but to work in the fossil fuel industry.

The bridge he spoke of was a "just transition" away from these jobs for tar sands workers.

A few months after he spoke those words, Fort McMurray was engulfed in flames.[2] The boreal forest surrounding the city burned for miles and miles, quickly spreading across 590,000 hectares. The whole area was evacuated and much of the city was destroyed, a direct result of climate change. The fire released 85 million tons of carbon dioxide equivalent emissions, or 10 percent of Canada's total carbon emissions. With damages estimated at C$9.9 billion, it was the costliest disaster in Canadian history.

According to scientists,[3] in order to keep global temperature rise under 2°C, Canada's estimated 2.2 trillion barrels of bitumen deposits must stay in the ground. Yet far from moving away from bitumen extraction, the Canadian government recently purchased Kinder Morgan's Trans Mountain pipeline for $4.5 billion. Pipelines are one of the primary ways bitumen is brought to refineries, and these pipelines cross First Nations lands.

Indigenous people are leading the fight to stop the rape of the planet and the violation of their ancestral lands. The Wet'suwet'en people of British Columbia, who have inhabited their territory from time immemorial, have taken a strong stand to defend their sovereignty. The hereditary leadership has refused to allow the Trans Mountain pipeline to be built across their territory. When the Royal Canadian Mounted Police (RCMP), working with both the British Columbia and Canadian governments, attacked the Unist'ot'en camp that had been set

2. https://en.wikipedia.org/wiki/2016_Fort_McMurray_wildfire

3. www.theguardian.com/environment/2015/jan/07/much-worlds-fossil-fuel-reserve-must-stay-buried-prevent-climate-change-study-says

up to stop the construction, solidarity demonstrations broke out across the country.[4]

There is still a chance that the worst consequences of climate change can be slowed down. But climate change is accelerating, and government and corporate responses are criminally slow or non-existent.

Hoping to spark a movement to force action, in 2015 film maker Avi Lewis and Naomi Klein, author of *This Changes Everything: Capitalism versus the Climate*, brought together 60 people from Indigenous communities, racialised groups, trade unions, and environmental organisations for two days of meetings in Toronto. The intent was to find common cause in the fight for climate justice. Most participants had never been in the same room together and there were hard discussions. The result was the LEAP Manifesto,[5] a call for rapid transformative change in response to the climate crisis: "Canada can transition to a renewable-based economy in a way that changes our country for the better — achieving meaningful justice for First Nations, creating more and better jobs, restoring and expanding our social safety net, building a better food system, and reducing economic, gender and racial inequalities."

One of the authors of the present article took part in that meeting, and although the final result was a compromise, it clearly linked the climate crisis to the austerity agenda and the attacks by governments and corporations on people across the globe. It called capitalism into question. The manifesto was an important step forward.

Respect for Indigenous lands, the question of just transition for workers and who gets the climate jobs created must be a major part of the discussions that are taking place to tackle the climate crisis. The trade union leadership has been very slow to pick up the fight for climate justice. But rank and file members such as Ken Smith are trying to come to grips with the

4. *www.cbc.ca/news/indigenous/risk-assessment-wetsuweten-unistoten-camp-1.4975744*
5. *https://leapmanifesto.org/en/the-leap-manifesto/#manifesto-content*

contradictions they are facing, working in toxic environments for companies that both exploit them and the earth. Smith sees himself as a workers' advocate and has spoken on platforms with Indigenous activists fighting pipeline expansion, including at the Marxism Conference in Toronto.[6]

There are examples of workers putting forward solutions, such as the Canadian Union of Postal Workers (CUPW) which is calling for the creation of postal banking to fund green projects. It is also calling for transitioning Canada's largest truck fleet to electric power. As the CUPW president said, this could be done by retrofitting existing plants such as General Motors Oshawa, which is scheduled to be shut down with the loss of thousands of unionised jobs. Another example is the Fight for $15 and Fairness movement which is demanding decent wages for low carbon jobs.

The Green New Deal in the United States sets forth a plan for a national mobilisation to achieve net zero greenhouse gas emissions. At the same time, investments in infrastructure and carbon-free energy would develop millions of well-paying climate jobs in ten years. Included in this is prior consent from Indigenous people if their land is impacted in any way, as well as a just transition with wage and benefit guarantees for all workers that would be affected by the job losses. This proposal has already had a major impact on the political terrain in the United States.

A Canadian Green New Deal [7]is also being proposed, but with a recognition of the failings of the original New Deal in the US, which was put forward by President Roosevelt in the 1930s in response to strong movements of workers and the unemployed. It was a massive investment in infrastructure to put people back to work during the Depression and to co-opt the radical solutions advanced by organized socialists.

A Green New Deal is urgently needed today. It can provide a

6. *https://youtu.be/YhrY0Dvu9Ks*
7. *www.couragecoalition.ca/a-green-new-deal-of-the-north*

real alternative to the right-wing populism that is drawing many disaffected people to its cause and put forward progressive options for a better life that actually challenges capitalism itself.

This is a desperately needed opportunity for unions to go on the offensive against austerity. The workers' movement can be part of creating a broad campaign with Indigenous peoples and communities of colour to generate a massive number of new climate jobs for workers in the dying fossil fuel sector and for young people looking for good, union jobs as a pathway out of poverty.

As we write this, a growing climate movement is raising broader demands and important debates are taking place. In Quebec, university students are joining the secondary students in climate strikes. This is a moment to build strong alliances that can put workers in all our diversity, Indigenous people, youth and racialised communities first. It can become a movement that fights for economic, racial and social equality and take on the logic of the system. Organised socialists must be at the heart of this movement.

***

Chapter 10
Up Against the Clock: Climate, Social Movements and Marxism

Suzanne Jeffery

Time is running out. This is not an alarmist call to arms but a reflection of the scientific consensus about what is happening to the climate and what will happen in the coming years unless action to reduce emissions of greenhouse gases happens on a huge scale and begins now.[1]

The time frame is incredibly short. The problem is not one for future generations but for our generation, those of us who are alive now. If we continue to produce greenhouse gas emissions at the rate we have been, we will have used up the carbon needed to take us to 2°C warming in the next 30 years.[2] Governments have agreed repeatedly to aim to limit rises to 2°C, and more recently 1.5°C, above the pre-industrial average temperature. Above this rise, scientists fear feedback processes would

1. The Intergovernmental Panel on Climate Change (IPCC) Special Report October 2018, gives only 12 years to reduce emissions to stay below 1.5°C. See *www.ipcc.ch/sr15/* This chapter is an updated and expanded version of an article first published in *International Socialism* 148 (Autumn 2015).

2. This understanding of a carbon budget is part of the analysis of the IPCC but it has also been popularised in the influential and popular book *The Burning Question.* Mike Berners-Lee and Duncan Clark, *The Burning Question* (Profile Books, 2013).

be triggered, that would result in climate change becoming catastrophic and irreversible.[3] The current predictions from scientists are that without emissions being reduced and with a "business as usual" scenario, we are on track for 4 to 6 degrees of warming by the end of the century. Professor James Hansen, a leading climate scientist, former head of NASA's Goddard Institute for space studies and activist, describes 4 to 6 degrees of warming like this: "Four degrees of warming would be enough to melt all the ice... You would have a tremendously chaotic situation as you moved away from our current climate towards another one. That's a different planet. You wouldn't recognise it... We are on the verge of creating climate chaos if we don't begin to reduce emissions rapidly".[4]

Despite this, in the last few years the response of governments globally has been inaction at best and, at worst, policies that increase emissions. This predates the current economic crisis but it is also intimately connected with it. In September 2008 Lehman Brothers went bust. The UN climate talks in Copenhagen were only 15 months later, in December 2009. The result of the collapse of Lehman Brothers and the economic crisis it foretold has been the prolonged and destructive era of austerity during which governments have continued to push even more aggressively the policies and economic system that caused the crisis in the first place. Meanwhile the result of the Copenhagen talks, in part shaped by the economic crisis, was a catastrophic non-deal which led to governments around the world continuing wilfully to ignore the urgent need to reduce fossil fuel use. Instead they pushed the expansion of fossil fuels even more aggressively especially through non-conventional methods such as fracking. By 2019 the results

3. It also worth noting that this kind of warming is bringing with it catastrophic species extinction — Elizabeth Kolbert, *The Sixth Extinction: An Unnatural History* (Bloomsbury, 2014) and Ian Rappel, "Capitalism and Species Extinction", *International Socialism* 147, summer 2015, *http://isj.org.uk/capitalism-and-species-extinction/*

4. Quoted in Nafeez Ahmed, "James Hansen: Fossil Fuel Addiction Could Trigger Runaway Global Warming", *Guardian*, 10 July 2013, *www.theguardian.com/environment/earth-insight/2013/jul/10/james-hansen-fossil-fuels-runaway-global-warming*

for ordinary people of both these key historical moments have been devastating. The impact of austerity on the lives of ordinary people has been dramatic. Similarly, the consequences of the failure to tackle rising emissions are frightening.

These twin and connected crises require a huge challenge to the system in order to bring about the kind of changes necessary to organise society to benefit ordinary people and safeguard the climate of the planet we live on. Fortunately, in recent years there has been a growing and increasingly radical climate movement.

The growing climate movement

One important expression of the strength of the climate movement has been the number of big climate demonstrations. In September 2014 there were significant demonstrations in towns and cities across the world, supported by major NGOs as well as many smaller grassroots organisations. These protests were organised to coincide with a UN summit on climate change and included a demonstration of 40,000 in London as well as a demonstration of 400,000, the biggest ever on climate change, in New York where the summit was held.[5]

In the UK in 2015 20,000 took part in the Time to Act demonstration in March of that year. Initiated by the small but active Campaign against Climate Change (CaCC), this demonstration, like the others, was young, vibrant, diverse and radical. As part of the demonstration, thousands took part in a sit-down along Whitehall. At the final rally, for the first time at a climate march, trade unionists spoke alongside social justice activists, anti-fracking campaigners, anti-austerity activists and anti-racists as well as politicians and representatives of some of the leading NGOs.[6]

5. Melissa Davey, Adam Vaughan and Amanda Holpuch, "People's Climate March: Thousands Demand Action Around the World—as it happened", *Guardian*, 29 September 2014, *www. theguardian.com/environment/live/2014/sep/21/peoples-climate-march-live*

6. Karl Mathiesen, "Time to Act: Climate Change Protesters March in London", *Guardian*, 7 March 2015, *www.theguardian.com/environment/2015/mar/07/time-to-act-climate-change-protest-london*

The Time to Act demonstration was a significant sign of the potential of the movement. Despite the fact that it did not coincide with any major climate event acting as a focus for mobilisation and that it was organised by grassroots activists rather than any of the larger NGOs, it was a huge success that acted to further galvanise a growing movement with a radical message.

In Canada in the same year 25,000 took to the streets in Quebec for the Act on Climate demonstration in April. Then in July up to 15,000 people marched in Toronto. This was the largest environmental demonstration in Canadian history outside the province of Quebec. Similarly, for the first time on an environmental march, the Toronto demonstration brought together trade unionists, indigenous people, anti-poverty campaigners and pro-migrant groups. They marched under the slogan "Jobs, justice and climate action", calling for climate solutions that would make society fairer and making explicit the connection between climate and the wider social struggle. This demonstrated a major step forward for the climate movement. One organiser from an anti-poverty group called the march the "launch of a powerful new movement". Again across both demonstrations, marchers were young, diverse, angry and radical.[7]

Another sign of the growing movement has been the ongoing anti-fracking campaigns, with some scoring notable successes against companies such as Cuadrilla. In Balcombe in Sussex a high profile campaign in 2013, which included the setting up of a camp to block drilling, resulted in a great victory for campaigners. Cuadrilla backed off, claiming it would no longer be drilling as a result of the unsuitability of the area's geology. But the real message was not lost on anti-fracking groups across the country — action works. In Lancashire, with broad support from activists, trade unions, NGOs and councillors, an ongoing campaign at Preston New Road has successfully delayed fracking from commencing for many years. In doing so the campaign raised the profile of the fracking issue.

7. Martin Lukacs, "'Historic' Toronto Climate March Calls for New Economic Vision", *Guardian*, 6 July 2015, *http://tinyurl.com/qbbxv4e*

Although the site did begin fracking in late 2018, it has not yet become fully operational, dogged by continued protest, opposition and earthquake tremors.

One sign of the strength of the anti-fracking movement was the huge public response to the jailing of three anti-fracking protesters from Preston New Road. The long sentences and their political nature were clearly designed to intimidate the rising anti-fracking movement and resulted in a huge and successful campaign to quash the sentences, supported by academics, trade unionists and environmental groups. The anti-fracking movement in the UK continues to grow and has prevented the development and expansion of a UK fracking industry like that in the US.

In the US indigenous communities and campaigners have fought with unbelievable bravery against state brutality to stop fossil fuel pipelines. The actions of protesters at the Standing Rock Indian Reservation in North and South Dakota in 2016 epitomised the courage of those in opposition to the Dakota Access pipeline — as well as the barbarity of those determined to expand fossil fuel interests.

The continued growth of the movement calling for divestment from fossil fuels is another important illustration of what's happening in the climate movement. Research by Oxford University at the outset of the divestment campaign suggested that it had become the fastest growing in history, surpassing those against the tobacco industry and the South African apartheid regime.[8] The divestment movement has modelled its strategy on the success of the anti-apartheid movement and built real momentum. The aim is to embarrass institutions that invest in the companies extracting the fossil fuels that will destroy the planet. In addition, the campaign aims to show to investors that fossil fuels will be "stranded assets" if the move

8. Asif Ansar, Ben Caldecott and James Tilbury, "Stranded Assets and the Fossil Fuel Divestment Campaign: What does Divestment Mean for the Valuation of Fossil Fuel Assets?" Smith School of Enterprise and the Environment, October 2013, *www.smithschool.ox.ac. uk/research-programmes/stranded-assets/SAP-divestment-report-final.pdf*

to renewable energy required by the need to reduce emissions takes off. The highest profile corporate divestor is the Rockefeller Brothers Fund — it has withdrawn $86 million from fossil fuel investments.

The focus on winning corporate investors to turn away from "stranded assets" faces obvious challenges. Nevertheless the campaign has most energy and potential around the call on institutions which use public funds, such as universities and pension funds, to divest. On university campuses the divestment campaigns have grown quickly with some significant successes. Students have used many of the tactics of the anti-apartheid movement such as sit-ins and occupations to win gains. Despite its short life, important successes have been achieved with Glasgow University, SOAS, and the Universities of Warwick and Bedfordshire divesting from fossil fuel investments after lively campaigns. Local Councils have also begun to divest in response to campaigns and many divestment campaigns are keen to turn their attention to pension funds. There is also a growing movement around pushing for local councils to declare a climate emergency and ensure that council policies reflect this.[9]

Recent months have seen an escalation of protest action over climate change. Extinction Rebellion took to the streets after forming in the UK in 2018, mobilising tens of thousands in direct action events calling on government to recognise the climate emergency and act. In February 2019 UK school students in their thousands took their place in a global school student strike movement, inspired by the actions of Greta Thunberg, the Swedish school student who sat outside the Swedish parliament, initiating the #FridaysforFuture days of action. The school student strikes have now become a global movement with amazing scenes of tens of thousands of Australian school students in December 2018 striking on the eve of the UN climate talks (COP24), defying threats form government ministers. These strikes represent a qualitative leap forward in a

9. See *www.campaigncc.org/councils_climate_emergency*

growing climate movement, further galvanised by the urgency of the climate crisis and the inaction of politicians globally to respond to this crisis.

The success of Naomi Klein's book *This Changes Everything*, with its clear and radical message that tackling climate change means tackling capitalism, illustrates the potential of the movement, with huge sales of the book and big audiences for its ideas around the world.[10]

However, the climate movement is not universally radical and there are competing ideas in the movement. Many are pulling in a much more conservative direction, looking simply to lobby business or get the right politicians elected. But there is a growing section of the climate movement that sees the problem as rooted in the type of society we have. The solution for these people is to challenge that system and to challenge the powerful corporate interests that are blocking change. It is also true that the climate issue is beginning to be understood and engaged with by the wider movement for social change and equally many in the climate movement are beginning to recognise the common cause with those who are challenging the system across a range of struggles.

"System change not climate change" is a popular slogan and a good summation of the ideas of a section of the movement. What is meant by the "system" and hence what kind of change is needed, or indeed possible, is of course an area of debate. I will return to this point. However, the fact that there is an increasingly radical climate movement shaped to some extent by a radical critique of the system must be understood by the left.

One reason for the growth of this movement is the increased urgency of the crisis in the context of continuing inaction by those at the top of society. Indeed, worse than inaction, governments around the world have sometimes paid lip-service to the climate crisis while simultaneously pushing policies that expand fossil fuel extraction and use. The UK

10. Naomi Klein, *This Changes Everything* (Penguin Books, 2014).

coalition government of 2010 initially claimed that it would be "the greenest government ever". But despite the rhetoric, it was a loyal supporter of the fossil fuel industry — an industry that, as research by the World Development Movement has shown, many of its ministers had close links with.[11]

In spite of growing public opposition, the coalition supported fracking and the current Tory government has continued to push for a huge expansion of the industry.[12] Both the coalition government and the Tory governments granted subsidies to fossil fuel companies but cut those for renewable energy, significantly undermining the expansion of renewables. The Tories have scrapped subsidies for onshore wind farms altogether, effectively banning any new onshore wind farms from being built.

Increased temperatures, unusual seasonal weather and specific extreme weather events have been an alarm call for millions. Extreme weather events in recent years have demonstrated what changing weather patterns as a result of climate change might look like and the misery they will cause for the poorest people. Hurricane Sandy, the "superstorm" that hit New York in October 2012, acted as a wake-up call for many on the left, demonstrating how little governments, even in the wealthiest countries, would do to help the most vulnerable. As Naomi Klein movingly describes in her book, huge swathes of working class areas were left for days without any help or support from the state.[13] Although less dramatic, the storms and floods in the UK in 2014 also demonstrated to millions of people that those in power would do little to help ordinary people cope with extreme weather conditions.

Climate change is a social justice issue. With the climate

11. World Development Movement, "Web of Power: The UK Government and the Energy-finance Complex Fuelling Climate Change", March 2013, www.globaljustice.org.uk/sites/default/files/files/resources/web_of_power_media_briefing.pdf

12. Emma Howard, and David Hellier, "1,000 sq miles of England to be Opened up for Fracking", Guardian, 18 August 2015, www.theguardian.com/environment/2015/aug/18/1000-sq-miles-england-opened-up-fracking-new-round-licences

13. Klein, This Changes Everything, as above, pp103-105.

crisis, as with the economic crisis, governments globally and nationally have prioritised the interests of those who caused the problem, rather than those who disproportionately suffer the consequences and are often least able to cope with the effects. We are not "all in it together". An increased understanding of this has led the climate movement both to grow in size and to adopt more radical slogans.

The importance of climate jobs

The success of the *One Million Climate Jobs* campaign is one example of the deepening of the climate movement. The campaign was an initiative taken by the Campaign against Climate Change Trade Union group in 2009 coming out of a conference organised by the group. It produced a report, *One Million Climate Jobs*, outlining how the creation of certain types of jobs could rapidly cut emissions. The first edition of the report was published in 2009. In 2014 it was updated and reprinted for the third edition, which now has the backing of eight national unions.[14] In addition there have been eight national conferences aimed at rank and file trade unionists and a Climate Jobs Caravan tour of the country to promote, discuss and popularise the campaign. The success of the idea and campaign has led to similar initiatives in other countries.

The central role of the campaign is to demonstrate that there are solutions to our climate crisis. The report outlines clearly how the creation of jobs in renewable energy, public transport, home insulation, energy efficiency and other areas of the economy such as waste and agriculture could slash emissions by more than 80 percent over 20 years — actions that would tackle the climate crisis as well as creating jobs.

However, the campaign also plays a wider role. It has acted as a way of engaging with and winning the debate about climate among ordinary people and importantly within the organised

14. Campaign against Climate Change, *One Million Climate Jobs—Tackling the Environmental and Economic Crises* (Third edition, 2014). *www.campaigncc.org/sites/data/files/Docs/one_million_climate_jobs_2014.pdf*

working class. Winning support for climate jobs is not a narrow economic discussion playing to the supposed prejudices of trade unionists. It involves debate about the reality and causes of the climate crisis. It means engaging with ideas about the possibility or otherwise of tackling the problem. It can often mean an opportunity to challenge and defeat right wing climate sceptic ideas marshalled by the fossil fuel lobby and pumped out in some sections of the mass media.

It has been able to frame the climate debate in a way that doesn't accept that ordinary people are part of the problem. Most significantly, it begins to both assert the role that workers could have in solving the climate crisis — by doing meaningful, productive work — and the changes needed in society in order to allow workers to be part of the answer.

Allowing workers to be part of the solution raises further strategic questions. It is a lack of any kind of basic democratic control over the production process that blocks real solutions from being implemented. The climate jobs campaign asserts that democratic control of production through the creation of a National Climate Service is the only way to enable the real change needed.

Therefore climate jobs also act as a bridge to wider debates about the type of society we need and ways of achieving it and puts the working class at the heart of those debates. By putting the needs of the planet and those who live on it ahead of profit, it successfully exposes the failure of neoliberal capitalism to deliver something that is completely possible, both practically and technologically. In doing this it deepens and radicalises the movement.

This has meant that in a relatively short space of time the idea of climate jobs has become, if not an accepted common sense within the working class movement, then something that has this potential.

The *One Million Climate Jobs* report was pioneering. The premise that fighting for good, well paid, skilled jobs and tackling the environmental crisis are not mutually exclusive has established itself as part of the trade union and climate movement. This has been given greater momentum though initiatives such as the proposed Green New Deal (GND) in the US. Democrat politicians Alexandria Ocasio-Cortez and Ed Markey drew up the GND and submitted it as a resolution to the US Senate. The GND aims to meet 100 percent of the power needed by the US through clean, renewable and zero-emissions sources to achieve net-zero greenhouse gas emissions. The plan outlined aims to complete this transition through a ten-year national mobilisation that would "create millions of good, high-wage jobs".

There are differences between *One Million Climate Jobs* and the Green New Deal and there are a number of valid debates about the GND, including the extent to which the GND has committed to ending fossil fuel use. However this is a key moment, which opens possibilities of delivering the huge economic and social transformations necessary to restructure away from fossil fuels — possibilities that will only be realised if the social forces of the working class are able to mobilise behind these demands.

This is also a key moment because it pulls into the debate the organisations of the working class — the trade unions. Equally it exposes some of the faultlines within the unions. The position taken by unions has the potential to give huge social weight to build real momentum for a transition away from fossil fuels or act as a backward break on this.

There is huge popular and union support for the Green New Deal, which also addresses health and social issues. But some in the US trade union movement have responded with a sectional and backward response, describing the deal as "unrealistic". Seven energy sector unions expressed "grave concerns" about the unrealistic solutions advocated in the Green New Deal.

In the UK similar arguments against a transition to renewables and climate jobs have been made by some unions. The GMB union submitted a motion passed at TUC congress in 2018, which stated that the views of energy workers should be "paramount and central to development of all TUC policies on energy, industrial strategy and climate change". This position is a backward one that fails to recognise that climate change is a working class issue, one which affects us all, not just a narrow section of the working class who work in industries tied up with fossil fuels.

The unions putting such arguments tend to do so in the name of protecting jobs. They describe transition to renewables as "unrealistic" as a way to provide well-paid jobs and "unviable" as a means of meeting our energy needs, arguing instead that we need an "energy mix" to maintain jobs and "keep the lights on". They are wrong on both counts. The companies and politicians currently involved with saving and expanding the fossil fuel industry are not motivated by a desire to protect jobs — or to meet the energy needs of humanity, for that matter.

Calls for *One Million Climate Jobs*, a Green New Deal or a Just Transition are part of an offensive strategy to demand a transition from an energy system which is at the heart of a climate crisis for millions of ordinary people on the planet, to one which prioritises the needs of the majority, for a safe climate, an end to energy poverty, democratic control over the energy and transport systems and for good, well paid, skilled and unionised jobs.

More needs to be done, however, in order to ensure that this is the dominant position across the trade union movement. Ensuring that the *One Million Climate Jobs* campaign is raised in workplaces and union branches will allow these ideas to be engaged with and owned by the working class and wider movement, strengthening both the climate movement and the wider movement for social change.

Building a stronger movement

The growing climate movement should give us heart. The urgency of the situation gives a different dimension to the struggle. However, this urgency doesn't change everything. It doesn't remove the obstacles to achieving fundamental social change. These are the same obstacles that have stood in the way in the past and include both the power of the system and the difficulties of building a movement that can take on that system. So political and theoretical debate that can strengthen the movement must also be fundamental in the coming period. There are two related issues I would like to raise in the interest of deepening debate in order to strengthen the movement.

There is a tendency in the movement to underestimate the degree of concern among ordinary people about climate change and their willingness to take action, including action that affects people's personal lives. In a survey featured in the Observer in 2015, four-fifths (82 percent) of the population agreed that the global climate is changing; 72 percent believe that global climate change will pose a serious threat to global stability within the next 50 years. The survey also found that people do take action to reduce energy consumption, but believe that individual actions only have a limited impact and that governments should do more.[15] In the US recent polls have shown a surge in concern about global warming to record levels. [16]

Even when confronted with such evidence of the degree of public concern, many environmentalists either dismiss or under-estimate the significance of this, because surveys also show that other issues are often ranked higher as areas of concern above climate change. This is then taken as an indication that climate activists have lost the battle with the public. Of course climate change should be a top priority, but seeing any shift up the scale of public concern should be taken as an indication that building a broader and deeper movement is possible.

This failure to grasp the shift taking place can mean that activists spend large amounts of time focused on the question

15. Nicholas Stern, "Extreme weather and rising seas are already global threats. This will only intensify", *Observer Tech Monthly* climate change special, 1 May 2015, *www.theguardian. com/environment/2015/may/01/climate-change-nicholas-stern-paris-summit-global-warming*

16. Oliver Milman, "Americans' climate change concerns surge to record levels, poll shows", *Guardian*, 22 January 2019, *www.theguardian.com/environment/2019/jan/22/climate-change-concern-americans-poll*

of how to get the message over to people about climate change, driven by the presumption that people are not willing to engage with the issue. To some extent this fits with the preferred method of campaigning of many of the bigger NGOs, whose emphasis is on professional looking campaigns designed to support the lobbying of government. A danger of this is that it can pull towards a more conservative approach to campaigning in which radical arguments, both about the seriousness of the problem and about the solutions, are played down for fear of alienating potential supporters.

Countering the supposed lack of interest among the public is seen as the magic formula for success in the battle over climate. George Marshall's influential book, *Don't Even Think About It: Why Our Brains Are Wired to Ignore Climate Change*[17] takes this approach. Engaging in debates and winning people to activism is crucial, but this isn't helped by assuming that most people don't care. In fact, the potential for mass action is often written off or there is a pressure to water down radical messages, inhibiting rather than strengthening the movement.

Capitalism, growth and Marxism

The more radical wing of the movement is strongly influenced by anti-capitalist politics. The analysis tends to locate the problem with capitalism in its inherent drive for growth. So Naomi Klein talks about the system as one in which there is a ruthless drive for expansion, kept going by "consumption for consumption's sake".[18] For her the key features of the system we need to challenge are "the fundamental, growth based, profit seeking logic of capitalism".[19] Brian Morris praises Murray Bookchin and Barry Commoner, both important radical ecological thinkers, for their early identification (in the 1970s) of capitalism as the root of the ecological crisis because it was a system based

17. George Marshall, *Don't Even Think About It: Why Our Brains Are Wired to Ignore Climate Change* (Bloomsbury, 2014).

18. Klein, *This Changes Everything,* as above, p179.

19. Klein, as above, p89.

on putting profits before human need and seeing no limit to "industrial progress, no limit to growth and technology".[20]

Richard Smith says,

> The orthodox view of economists...from Adam Smith to Karl Marx [is] that growth is an iron law of capitalist development, that capitalism cannot exist without constant revolutionising of productive forces, without constantly expanding markets, without ever-growing consumption of resources. Indeed, it was precisely this market-propelled "motor" of economic development that for Karl Marx so sharply distinguished the capitalist mode of production from all previous historical modes of production.[21]

This drive for expansion and growth, inherent in capitalism, is destructive because it pushes up against the limits of the earth's resources. This analysis is correct. The rapacious and wasteful destruction of the earth's resources in pursuit of profit is a conspicuous aspect of capitalism. However, in this analysis only one contradiction within capitalism is identified — the contradiction between the drive for capital accumulation (growth) and the impact on the earth's resources — what John Bellamy Foster (following Marx) calls the "ecological rift".[22]

But emphasis only on this contradiction can tend to downplay other important contradictions within capitalism that unlock the potential for challenging the system. It can also put the weight of explanation for the dynamics of capitalism at the level of consumption without understanding how consumption is structured by production.

This can result in mistakenly seeing workers as having a

20. Brian Morris, *Anthropology, Ecology, and Anarchism: A Brian Morris Reader* (PM Press, 2014), p191.

21. Richard Smith, "Beyond Growth or Beyond Capitalism?", *Truthout*, 15 January 2014, *www.truth-out.org/news/item/21215-beyond-growth-or-beyond-capitalism*

22. John Bellamy Foster, *Marx's Ecology: Materialism and Nature* (Monthly Review Press, 2000).

material stake in the system. If the system is one of perpetual growth, then it can appear that both capitalists and workers have a vested interest in the continuation of this system. Richard Smith articulates this well and no doubt reflects the views of many when he says:

> What's more, given capitalism, we're all more or less locked into this lemming-like suicidal drive to hurl ourselves off the cliff. Whether as CEOs, investors, workers or governments, given capitalism, we all "need" to maximise growth, therefore to consume more resources and produce ever more pollution in the process—because companies need to satisfy the insatiable demands of investors and because we all need the jobs. That's why at every UN Climate Summit the environment is invariably sacrificed to growth.[23]

Capitalism generates growth, but it also generates crisis. Capitalism is a system of accumulation in competition and it is as a result of this competition that there is an inherent drive for expansion and also an inherent drive to crisis. Both are equally destructive, socially and environmentally. Capitalism both destroys the earth's resources in expansion and lays waste to them in crisis. So capitalism is simultaneously a system of destructive expansion and of destructive contraction. Ordinary people tend to experience both, the expansion and crisis, and mostly this is experienced as insecurity and fear, which is why it can ring hollow when the problem of capitalism is simply explained as a problem of growth.

Within capitalism the producers — workers — are separated from the means of production and their ability to work has become a commodity. This commodity is purchased and put to use by capitalists, driven by their need to accumulate for

23. Richard Smith, "Climate Crisis, the Deindustrialization Imperative and the Jobs vs Environment Dilemma", *Truthout*, 12 November 2014, *https://truthout.org/articles/climate-crisis-the-deindustrialization-imperative-and-the-jobs-vs-environment-dilemma/* (emphasis in the original).

accumulation's sake and to compete with each other. So, fundamentally, the workers who produce the wealth in society do not own or control that wealth and do not generally have a say in what is produced or how. Humans' ability to labour to shape the world around them, is not driven by human need but by the needs of the market and the capitalists who exploit that ability.

This contradiction ensures that, while capitalists seek to defend the system that enriches them, workers have an objective interest in ending the system of capitalism and establishing new social relations that allow production to be regulated in the interests of the many and the planet rather than the few. Workers and capitalists have objectively different interests and this is why Marx called the working class the gravediggers of the system.

A more complete understanding of the dynamics of capitalism and the contradictions at the heart of the system could play an important part in strengthening and deepening the climate movement. It would help ensure that a grassroots movement recognises that the working class is part of the solution with an objective interest in overthrowing the system rather than propping it up.

The Paris agreement and beyond
In the run up to the protests at the Paris climate talks of December 2015 there was concern among activists that the mobilisation would repeat the mistakes of previous mobilisations, especially those for the Copenhagen climate talks in 2009, which many argued had allowed the majority of the movement to put misplaced faith in the willingness of politicians to deliver a positive outcome at the talks. This raised concerns that demonstrators were being used simply as a stage army to support the lobbying efforts of the bigger NGOs. Hence when the talks failed in the disastrous Copenhagen protocol of 2009, the movement had also collapsed in demoralisation at the failure of the talks.[24]

24. Jonathan Neale, "Climate Politics after Copenhagen", *International Socialism* 126, spring 2010, *http://isj.org.uk/climate-politics-after-copenhagen*

Many of those tensions continued in 2015. Prior to Paris Patrick Bond critiqued the nature of some of those tensions deriving from a strategy of "unity-seeking minus politics" pushed by many of the bigger NGOs in the movement. He identified how a similar approach in Durban in 2011 resulted in a demonstration that South African political leaders could use to legitimise their actions and a failure to build a movement coming out of the summit. He went on to argue that without an agreed radical narrative a similar failure to hold the governments to account could be the outcome of the Paris mobilisations.[25]

However, in many ways the movement going into the Paris 2015 mobilisations was in much better shape than that which had mobilised for Copenhagen. This ensured that regardless of the grandiose claims and headlines which greeted the Paris Agreement in 2015, the movement was neither duped, derailed nor demobilised.

Bond's concerns and analysis were right. But there were also more fundamental processes in play in terms of the direction and strength of the movement that ensured that the outcome of the Paris talks did not derail the movement. Large sections of the movement understood that governments are not willing to deliver the action necessary to tackle climate change. Many in the movement understood that the Paris agreement was historic only in so far as it underlined what the movement has been arguing for years — that there is an urgent and real threat to the climate that will have catastrophic consequences — but understood that the Paris agreement did absolutely nothing to prevent or tackle this climate crisis.

The commitments made by countries at Paris to reduce emissions, far from keeping temperatures below 1.5 degrees instead set us on track for 3 degrees warming, commitments that were voluntary rather than legally binding on countries. Despite the rhetoric there was no urgency in the agreement. The real action that could tackle climate change — massive

25. Patrick Bond, "Climate Movement across Movements", *Telesur*, 26 March 2015, *www. telesurenglish.net/opinion/Climate-Movement-Across-Movements-20150326-0035.html*

cuts to fossil fuels — were postponed by timelines which bore no relation to the pace of change that the climate was already undergoing.

Talks in Katowice, Poland in 2018 followed the same pattern with a massive gap between the urgent need for action and the inaction written into final agreements which ended the talks.

Government leaders at the talks are not willing to agree to the huge and rapid cuts in emissions needed to decarbonise the economy and which challenge the vested interests of significant sections of global capitalism. They are not willing to sacrifice the advantages of their own national economies over other countries regardless of what is at stake. They haven't done so in over two decades of talks and didn't at Paris or Katowice. This is already understood by many people within the movement. Therefore, unlike in Copenhagen, mobilising around the UN climate talks is not seen as an end point, but as only one aspect of building the kind of climate movement capable of delivering the necessary change.

In many countries a climate movement is developing that is broader and is beginning to have deeper roots in the working class and wider social movements, as well as its traditional base with the climate justice and direct action movement. In June 2015 the 250,000 strong People's Assembly demonstration in London saw climate activists demonstrate alongside the anti-austerity movement. The coalition working together to build the London demonstration on 29 November in the run-up to the Paris talks eventually agreed, after much debate, to march under the banner of the "People's March for Climate, Justice and Jobs", ensuring that a radical social narrative was at the heart of the demonstration. This compares with the title of the 2009 Copenhagen demonstration, "London Stop Climate Chaos — The Wave" which had little political content to it. These were very important developments.

On recent anti-racist demonstrations delegations of climate activists raising the issue of climate refugees have been supported and embraced by the wider anti-racist movement.

On the anti-Trump demonstrations in the UK in 2018, climate was one of the key stands of the huge mobilisations on the day, with activists from Campaign against Climate Change and other environmental groups playing a central role in the organisation of the mobilisations. The climate issue is increasingly a central part of the wider struggle. The issue of climate change is no longer the domain of committed environmentalists. It is now a key and increasingly central thread running through the wider movement for social change.

There is a lot at stake and the need to build a vibrant and radical climate movement that can play a central part in challenging the system at the root of our climate crisis is more urgent than ever. A mass, grassroots movement is needed which is rooted in support among the trade unions and the working class; one which recognises that mass action has the power to win; a movement that is ready to make common cause with other struggles against the system; one that has "system change not climate change" at the centre of its understanding.

This understanding must recognise that the system of capitalism lies at the heart of the climate crisis and that capitalism needs to be overthrown and replaced with a system that prioritises the needs of the planet over profit and which replaces the anarchic and destructive market with democratic planning. The left has a vital part to play in this movement. It's time for us all to play our part. Our success is being measured against a ticking clock.

***

Chapter 11
Can We Build a Sustainable Society?

Martin Empson

In December 2015 world leaders, who are signatories to the UN framework on climate change, met in Paris at the 21st annual Conference of the Parties (COP21) .[1] The Paris Agreement as it became known was lauded by politicians as laying out significant action on climate change. Yet the agreement signed in Paris, and those signed at subsequent conferences in Marrakech, Bonn and Katowice offered little real change. In the aftermath of the talks leading UK climate scientist Kevin Anderson argued that even if all the voluntary commitments made in Paris were adhered to, there would likely still be a three or four-degree temperature rise.

Such a rise will not simply lead to a warmer world; it will mean environmental disaster. Such a rise will make runaway climate change more likely and cause major sea-level rises with flooding on a huge scale. Hunger, famine and war will likely follow. Millions of people will face devastation.

In response to this the environmental movement is growing.

---

1. This is an updated version of an article that first appeared in *Socialist Review*, December 2015.

Protests and meetings are larger and tackling big questions. One example of this is the way that trade unions and campaigners across the world are taking up the idea of "climate jobs" as an alternative to climate chaos and austerity. At the same time there is a growing sense within the climate movement that we have to move beyond tinkering with the existing system. One example of this is the popularity of Naomi Klein's bestselling book, *This Changes Everything.* Subtitled *"Capitalism Versus the Climate"* the book succinctly summarises many environmentalists' thinking — the problem is the system, rather than technology, population growth or the wrong diet. Klein locates the climate crisis within a systemic critique of capitalism, a critique that fits directly with the experience that many of us have of austerity politics.

But what is less clear is what a sustainable alternative to capitalism would look like. One frustration I found reading Klein's book is that her alternative is not actually that different. It is a different capitalism, but it is still capitalism — more localised, more rational. Production is planned through state intervention designed to reduce greenhouse gas emissions at the same time as being more socially just. But it is still capitalism.

Capitalism as a system has at its core competing blocks of capital that strive to maximise their profits through the exploitation of workers. Because this production is based upon the natural world, it has an impact — the environmental degradation of nature through the extraction of resources and the creation of pollution, including emissions of carbon dioxide and other greenhouse gases.

Klein is right then to condemn this ecologically unsound system, particularly its "extractive industries" that she sees as being at the heart of the problem. But even if we could challenge the system and destroy the fossil fuel industry at the heart of capitalism, we would still leave in place a system based on the exploitation of workers and the competitive accumulation of wealth for the sake of accumulation.

Since the COP21 conference there have been intense

discussions about the way forward for the environmental movement. These have been exacerbated by the election of right-wing politicians like Donald Trump whose policies have begun to undo even the limited action that has been implemented. In August 2017 Trump announced that he was withdrawing the US from the Paris Agreement.

Revolutionary socialists must be at the heart of these debates. We want to build a bigger and stronger climate movement, but we also have something to offer — a vision of an alternative to capitalism based on the needs and interests of the vast majority of the population. Demonstrating this means exploring again some of the ideas of Marx and Engels.

At the core of the Marxist critique of capitalism is an understanding of the dialectical relationship between humans and the natural world. Karl Marx and Frederick Engels offered a critique of capitalism, but they also explored the way that communism, the society that they envisaged arising out of the revolutionary destruction of capitalism, would also be an ecologically sustainable world.

Unfortunately, many environmentalists dismiss the idea of socialism as a sustainable alternative to capitalism. Part of the problem is the experience of regimes like the Soviet Union, those in Eastern Europe or countries such as China. The leaders of these countries often used the language of socialism and Marxism, yet the central dynamic of production was geared, not towards the interests of workers and peasants, but towards competition with the West. The environmental record of the Soviet Union and the Eastern bloc was appalling, and China continues today to have huge problems with pollution.

The problematic relationship between these societies and the natural world is summed up best by two quotes, one from a Soviet economic planner who called for "a profound rearrangement of the entire living world...all living nature will live, thrive and die at none other than the will of man and according to his plans". More simply Chinese Communist Party leader Mao Zedong demanded that "man must conquer nature".

So it is no surprise that some on the left of the environmental movement might want to distance themselves from this. In his 2003 book, *Heat*, activist George Monbiot wrote that "the need to tackle climate change must not become an excuse for central planning".

But the relationship between society and nature outlined in the thinking of Marx and Engels was far from the crude ideas expressed by Soviet planners, or Mao. Their vision of socialism was one where the use and allocation of resources and the planning of society's production was done not by a centralised leadership, but by democratic decision-making involving the maximum number of concerned people.

In *Capital* Karl Marx argued for a vision of communism that was what we would now call sustainable:

> From the standpoint of a higher economic form of society, private ownership of the globe by single individuals will appear quite as absurd as private ownership of one man by another. Even a whole society, a nation, or even all simultaneously existing societies taken together, are not the owners of the globe. They are only its possessors, its usufructuaries, and, like boni patres familias [Good Heads of Household], they must hand it down to succeeding generations in an improved condition.

Marx's vision of communism arises in part from his critique of capitalism. He argued that capitalism was born "dripping in blood from every pore", and an essential part of this process was the separation of the majority of the population from their link to the land, "the original source of all wealth". What makes us human is our ability to labour on nature and change it in our interests. Under capitalism workers have become alienated from the natural world.

This "metabolic rift" is one of the key problems in the relationship between society and the natural world under capitalism. Healing this rift is an essential part of the transition to a more sustainable future. Marx talked about the way that once this separation is established it will continue and develop "until a new and fundamental revolution in the mode of production should again overturn it, and restore the original union in a new historical form".

What Marx is describing here is a society which heals the fundamental relationship between humans and nature, but not through a return to an older form of society. Instead a new society must be built. This requires the taking of property into social ownership through the process of revolution. Marx called this new form of society communism, a term inaccurately associated with the regimes that were established in the aftermath of Stalin's victory in the Soviet Union.

Under a genuine communist society, production would become transformed. Under capitalism production is for profit. Manufacturing is based on whether goods can be sold to make money, rather than whether or not they are needed by wider society. In 2009 one of the world's leading wind turbine manufacturers closed its plant on the Isle of Wight. Hundreds of jobs were lost at a time when the world was crying out for wind turbines to expand renewable energy. This was not because of a downturn of orders, quite the contrary — orders were booming — but because it would be more profitable for the company to manufacture wind turbines in China or the United States.

This emphasis on production for profit means that capitalism is incredibly wasteful of resources. Products that are profitable are manufactured in vast quantities, until there is a glut on the market and a crisis of over-production occurs. Witness the pictures of tens of thousands of unsold cars in manufactures' storage areas, each unsaleable car representing wasted raw materials, energy and labour. At the same time the world needs more coaches, buses and trains to expand and improve low carbon transport.

Marx's vision of production under communism was very

different. Writing in the aftermath of the 1871 Paris Commune he said, "United co-operative societies are to regulate national production upon a common plan, thus taking it under their own control and putting an end to the constant anarchy and periodical convulsions which are the fatality of capitalist production." It is a vision that still sounds radical and farsighted.

This democratically planned production is inherently sustainable because at its heart is the way that ordinary people plan and organise their interaction with the natural world. Freed from the restrictions of capitalism, which insists that workers view their labour through the prism of a world geared towards profit, workers could instead collectively plan their work in the interests of wider society.

A society that also ensured that those same workers had access to proper education would mean that, for the first time, workers could see their part of the production process as part of a wider interaction between society and nature.

When Marx and Engels discussed these questions they often looked at the way that, under capitalism, production had been concentrated into huge, polluting towns separated from the wider countryside. This meant an enormous waste of resources as goods and raw materials were transported around.

Engels noted how a rational society would begin to abolish this separation, and central to this were workers "with an all-round development who understand the scientific basis of industrial production as a whole, and each of whom has had practical experience in a whole series of branches of production from start to finish. This society will bring into being a new productive force which will abundantly compensate for the labour required to transport raw materials and fuel from great distances."

Some critics of Marx and Engels suggest that one problem with their vision of communism is that it sees the natural world as an inexhaustible collection of resources. But Marx and Engels were materialists who were fascinated by the latest scientific discoveries and technological developments. They understood that the problem was the way that capitalism related to the natural world in an unsustainable way.

One way that Marx examined this was to explore the question of capitalist agriculture. Geared towards the maximisation of profits rather than feeding hungry people, agriculture in Marx's time was suffering environmental crisis in the form of the degradation of the soil as nutrients were removed from the land but not replaced.

A scientific agriculture was possible through the use of fertilisers to revitalise the land. But the barrier to a rational agriculture was not technological, but social. Farmers who couldn't afford fertiliser could only continue by further destroying the soil, or going bankrupt. At the same time people went hungry because they couldn't afford food.

How would a new society come about? Marx and Engels based their understanding on the way that engaged in class struggle workers created their own organisations to help organise their fight. These might start as strike committees, but they had the potential to become organisations that could run society from the bottom up. Marx's understanding of this particularly developed through seeing and building solidarity with the Paris Commune when workers rose up and created the world's first, short-lived, workers' state in the French capital.

Since then revolutionaries have witnessed countless other examples of how workers engaged in struggle begin to take control of their own lives. We see examples in every fight that workers take part in. Strike committees might first organise pickets, but they might go on to challenge for leadership of their dispute, if, for instance, the trade union's leadership is not fighting the way the workers want.

At the heights of struggle, during revolutions, workers form networks of committees, based on democratically elected delegates from workplaces and communities. These councils are part and parcel of the struggle itself. But in revolutionary times they may take charge of organising food distribution, or the defence of the revolution itself; so they represent the living interests of workers. These revolutionary councils can form the basis for a new way of organising society.

The alternative to capitalism arises out of the struggle against capitalism. But what is important about this is not just the way that the new society is born, and how it is organised. It is also about how workers transform themselves in the process. As Marx put it:

> Both for the production on a mass scale of this communist consciousness, and for the success of the cause itself, the alteration of men on a mass scale is necessary, an alteration which can only take place in a practical movement, a revolution; this revolution is necessary, therefore, not only because the ruling class cannot be overthrown in any other way, but also because the class overthrowing it can only in a revolution succeed in ridding itself of all the muck of ages and become fitted to found society anew.

This creation of a "communist consciousness" means that workers remake themselves and put themselves back in their rightful place, as a part of nature, labouring and changing the world around them in the collective interest of people and planet, rather than as atomised consumers relating to nature through an alienated labour process.

Marx and Engels did not know about global climate change, though they understood that capitalism brought with it environmental crisis. Their vision of a communist society takes on a new importance in the 21st century as we see the inability of capitalism to deal with environmental disaster.

***

Further Reading

In recent years there has been an explosion of material related to the environment. In this section we list some recommended books that will enable the reader to develop their understanding of the topics covered.

The best introduction to the current climate crisis is Naomi Klein's *This Changes Everything: Capitalism versus the Climate* (Penguin, 2015) which locates the blame squarely with the capitalist system.

Martin Empson's pamphlet *Marxism and Ecology: Capitalism, Socialism and the Future of the Planet* (SWP, 2016) is an introductory guide to these ideas. His book *Land and Labour: Marxism, Ecology and Human History* (Bookmarks, 2014) looks at the changing relationship between humanity and nature and argues that Marxism is central to the struggle for a sustainable world.

Ian Angus's book *Facing the Anthropocene* (Monthly Review, 2016) is an excellent introduction to Anthropocene science from a Marxist perspective. Ian Angus and Simon Butler's *Too Many People?* (Haymarket, 2011) argues against those who say that over-population is the cause of environmental crisis and hunger.

Most of Karl Marx and Frederick Engels' work can be found online at the Marxist Internet Archive. An excellent introduction to Marx's work *Capital* is Joseph Choonara's *A Readers' Guide to Capital* (Bookmarks, 2017). John Bellamy Foster has written extensively on the ecological core to Marx's work. His book *Marx's Ecology* (Monthly Review, 2000) is his most important work. Foster's book *The Ecological Revolution* (Monthly Review, 2009) is an accessible work that looks at the relevance of Marx's ideas to environmental crises. *The Ecological Rift* (Monthly Review, 2011) by Foster, Brett Clarke and Richard York begins with an examination of the environmental crises and a critique of the mainstream solutions, arguing for a universal revolt against the system. Hannah Holleman's *Dustbowls of*

Empire (Yale, 2018) is a brilliant use of metabolic rift theory to understand the Dust Bowl of the 1930s and how a racist and class divided society exacerbated the impact of the disaster; and draw lessons for the 21st century.

In *The Political Economy of Global Warming: The Terminal Crisis* (Routledge, 2014), Del Weston uses metabolic rift theory to explain the failure of international agencies and national governments to respond effectively to the global climate crisis.

Three important but challenging books further develop the ecological critique that Marx developed. Paul Burkett's *Marx and Nature* (Haymarket, 2014) and his *Marxism and Ecological Economics* (Haymarket, 2009) detail the ecological implications of Marx's major economic works. Kohei Saito's *Karl Marx's Ecosocialism: Capital, Nature and the Unfinished Critique of Political Economy* (Monthly Review, 2017) is a detailed study of how Marx developed his core ideas around ecology and political economy, drawing in particular on his unpublished notebooks.

There are many books that describe the biodiversity crisis. A good overview is Elizabeth Kolbert's *The Sixth Extinction* (Bloomsbury, 2015). Ashley Dawson's book *Extinction: A Radical History* (OR, 2016) locates the biodiversity crisis in the framework of capitalist relations. Rachel Carson's classic book *Silent Spring* is credited with kick-starting the environmental movement. More than 50 years after its first publication it retains its power and its critique of the way that "the right to make a dollar at whatever cost is seldom challenged."

Philip Lymbery's highly readable *Farmageddon: The True Cost of Cheap Meat* (Bloomsbury 2015) written with Isabel Oakeshott and his *Dead Zone: Where the Wild Things Were* (Bloomsbury, 2018) examine the contribution that industrial agriculture makes to the destruction of biodiversity. One of the best Marxist critiques of the capitalist food system is Fred Magdoff and Brian Tokar's *Agriculture and Food in Crisis: Conflict, Resistance, and Renewal* (Monthly Review, 2010). Fred Magdoff and Chris Williams's *Creating an Ecological Society* (Monthly Review, 2017) is a look at how an ecologically sustainable, equitable and democratic society might come about. Ashley Dawson's *Extreme Cities* (Verso, 2019) shows how capitalism continues to develop unsustainable urban areas where neo-liberal policies, poverty, racism and inequality will exacerbate climate catastrophe. Richard Heinberg's book *Snake Oil: How Fracking's False Promise of Plenty Imperils our Future* (Clairview, 2014) focuses most on the US but its arguments against fracking are applicable everywhere. Okbazghi Yohannes's *The Biofuels Deception: Going Hungry on the Green Carbon Diet* (Monthly Review, 2019), demolishes the idea that biofuels are an energy alternative to fossil fuels and argues that they are a continuation of the same destructive accumulation strategy by the multinationals.

Andreas Malm's *Fossil Capital* (Verso, 2015) is an essential read to understand how the capitalism evolved as a fossil fuel system. His book *The Progress of This Storm: On the Dialectics of Society and Nature in a Warming World* (Verso, 2018) is a trenchant defence of Marxism as a method for understanding ecology in the context of recent critiques from the left.

Victor Wallis's *Red-Green Revolution: The Politics and Technology of Ecosocialism* (Political Animal Press, 2018) is a powerful argument for radical socialist politics that discusses the way that science and technology under capitalism is distorted by the profit motive, and looks at how this might be different in a socialist society. Ian Angus's *A Redder Shade of Green* (Monthly Review, 2017) looks at Marxism and science; including studies of the Red Chemist Carl Schorlemmer and Marx, Engels and Darwin to show how Marxists must root their analysis in scientific reality. *The Dialectical Biologist* (Harvard, 1985) and *Biology Under the Influence* (Monthly Review, 2007) were written by practising scientists Richard Levins and Richard Lewontin, and show the importance of dialectics for scientists trying to understand natural, and social processes.

***